CHEMICAL EQUILIBRIUM

CHEMICAL EQUILIBRIUM

CARL J. NYMAN

RANDALL E. HAMM

PROFESSORS OF CHEMISTRY
WASHINGTON STATE UNIVERSITY

RAYTHEON EDUCATION COMPANY

LIBRARY OF CONGRESS CATALOG CARD NUMBER 67-16910

PRINTED IN THE UNITED STATES OF AMERICA

Preface

Chemical equilibrium is a subject now universally treated in introductory chemistry textbooks and this brief monograph is intended as a supplement to the material encountered under the various conventional headings. The topics presented here have been selected so that students may read about several types of equilibria in some depth and perhaps obtain a better knowledge of both the equilibrium and nonequilibrium states.

On numerous occasions, students have asked the authors, "How can I find out if a reaction will occur between these substances?" and, "Why does this reaction go?" To answer the first question, one must know something about the rate at which the reaction is likely to occur and also something about the equilibrium constant for the reaction. To answer the second, information must be available on energy and entropy changes associated with the reaction. As a result of studying chemical equilibria, it is hoped the student will be able to answer for himself, three questions: (1) To what extent does the reaction approach completion? (2) How is the extent of reaction influenced by factors such as temperature, pressure, concentration, and catalysts? (3) What are the free energy, heat, and entropy changes accompanying the reaction?

After a brief discussion of kinetics and reaction rates, an introduction to the method of determining the extent of reaction from equilibrium constants is presented. Next the relationship of equilibrium constants and the thermodynamic functions $\Delta H°$, $\Delta G°$, and $\Delta S°$ are given with a brief discussion of their significance. It should be emphasized that it has not been our intention to derive thermodynamic quantities with complete rigor; rather, we have tried to show how they are related to chemical reactions. Detailed discussion of various types of equilibria, the information to be gained from them, and their significance follow in the latter chapters.

In general the subject matter has been organized to facilitate progression from the simpler to the more complicated systems. It is assumed, however, that the student has a knowledge of such concepts as moles, concentrations, the ideal gas law, chemical reactions, balancing equations, and stoichiometry as presented in an introductory course. The treatment is somewhat more rigorous than most introductory texts in that mass and charge balances are used to solve problems. Approximations and simplifications are made only after the rigorous balances have been established. Toward the end of each chapter, a detailed discussion of one or more applications of the type of equilibrium under discussion is included, with the purpose of illustrating the importance of these concepts to the science that is chemistry. A few illustrative unsolved problems are included for those students who may wish to test their newly acquired knowledge.

Students who read and study this book will have a better understanding of the complex subject of equilibria than they might otherwise. Hopefully, they will be prepared to attack and solve chemical problems of an equilibrium nature with some degree of confidence.

The authors would like to express their appreciation to Professors John C. Bailar, Jr., Jacob Kleinberg, Harold W. Dodgen, and Karl H. Pool who made many helpful suggestions.

PULLMAN, WASHINGTON   *Carl J. Nyman*
                                                       Randall E. Hamm

Contents

At our present state of knowledge, we know that a chemical equilibrium exists in a system when opposing chemical reactions occur with equal rates. In an equilibrated system containing the gases carbon monoxide, bromine, and carbonyl bromide, the rate at which carbonyl bromide is formed from carbon monoxide and bromide is exactly equal to the rate at which it decomposes to reform the reactants. This reaction is a reversible one and is most readily represented by the equation

$$CO(g) + Br_2(g) \rightleftharpoons COBr_2(g) \qquad \text{1-1}$$

When both forward and reverse reactions occur at the same rate, no net changes in the concentrations (or partial pressures) occur with the passage of time. Once the true equilibrium state has been achieved by a system in a closed vessel at constant temperature, no changes in the concentrations of reactants or products will occur.

The statement that a chemical equilibrium involves opposing reactions implies that in the above case the same equilibrium mixture may be obtained by starting with carbon monoxide and bromine, or by starting with carbonyl bromide. If one mole of carbon monoxide and one mole of bromine are introduced into a one liter container at 80°C, it is found after a period of time that 0.55 mole of carbon monoxide and 0.55 mole of bromine remain, and that 0.45 mole of carbonyl bromide has been formed. The introduction of one mole of carbonyl bromide into a similar one liter container at the same temperature, eventually produces the same amounts of the three species after the passage of enough time for equilibrium to be established.

An indication of the dynamic nature of chemical equilibrium is shown by the result of the following experiment. To one liter of an equilibrium mixture of carbon monoxide, bromine, and carbonyl bromide gases prepared in either of the above ways, a small amount of $C^{14}O$ is added. This quantity must be sufficiently small that its addition will have a negligible effect on the equilibrium concentrations of the three species. After a relatively short period of time, it will be found by appropriate sampling of the carbon monoxide that 55% of the added carbon-14 is in the form of carbon monoxide and 45% of the carbon-14 is in the form of carbonyl bromide. This is the same proportion as the concentrations of carbon monoxide and carbonyl bromide in the equilibrium mixture. By consideration of the rate of conversion of $C^{14}O$ to carbonyl bromide, the reaction here can be identified with that represented by Eq. 1-1.

The reaction just described obviously does not "go to completion," but occurs until a particular set of concentrations is attained. From the equilibrium conditions, the reaction shown by Eq. 1-1 occurs to an extent of 45% based on the moles of either carbon monoxide or bromine added. The reverse or dissociation reaction shown by the equation

$$COBr_2(g) \rightleftharpoons CO(g) + Br_2(g) \qquad \text{1-2}$$

occurs to the extent of 55%.

It is with a more detailed understanding of systems such as these that we are concerned. We shall learn to describe such systems quantitatively in terms of "equilibrium constants," and we shall learn that once the equilibrium constants are known, they may be used to calculate the extents of various chemical reactions.

Some reactions, such as the decomposition of hydrogen peroxide in aqueous acidic solution

$$2 H_2O_2(aq) \rightarrow 2 H_2O(aq) + O_2(g) \qquad \text{1-3}$$

appear to "go to completion." This reaction occurs at a measurable rate at room temperature and one atmosphere pressure. On mixing water and oxygen gas under the same conditions, no detectable amount of hydrogen peroxide is produced and so the decomposition reaction is considered to be irreversible.

One might argue that, in principle, all reactions in a closed system are reversible to some extent. However, one would have to wait an infinite time to observe any indication of the reverse reaction in a large number of cases.

2

Reaction Rates and Equilibrium Constants

2–A REACTION RATES

A wide range of chemical reaction rates is encountered. Some reactions appear to be extremely rapid, instantaneous, and too fast to measure. Others appear to be very slow and likewise almost impossible to measure. Between these two extremes lie the large number of chemical reactions whose rates are readily determined through various experimental techniques.

In the middle of the 19th century, research workers such as Güldberg, Waage, Van't Hoff, Berthelot, and Arrhenius, began to recognize the factors that affect rates of chemical reactions. Most readers are already qualitatively familiar with the effects of concentration, temperature, pressure, and catalysts on the rate with which a given chemical reaction occurs and with which it approaches equilibrium. These topics are of great importance to the subject of reaction kinetics. We intend to review some aspects of kinetics briefly and present some elementary mathematical relations. For a detailed discussion of the subject, the reader is referred to the monograph by Professor Gordon Harris entitled *Chemical Kinetics*. (See *Some Suggested Reading* in Appendix V.)

1 Effect of Concentration

It has been found that the initial rate of any chemical reaction is some function of the concentrations of the reacting species. One chemical reaction whose rate can be measured is that between hydrogen and iodine gases to form hydrogen iodide gas

$$H_2(g) + I_2(g) \rightarrow 2\,HI(g) \qquad \text{2-1}$$

When mixtures of hydrogen and iodine are investigated experimentally, the rate of formation of hydrogen iodide is found to be proportional to the first power of the concentration of hydrogen gas and to the first power of the concentration of iodine gas. Expressed mathematically this is formulated as

$$R_f = k_f[H_2][I_2] \qquad \text{2-2}$$

where R_f is the rate of formation of hydrogen iodide, k_f is a proportionality constant known as the specific reaction rate constant, and the bracketed symbols represent the concentrations of the species enclosed. Equation 2-2 is known as the *rate law* or *rate equation* for the reaction. For simple bimolecular reactions, those involving only two molecules, the exponents in the rate equation are the same as the coefficients of the substances in the balanced chemical equation. For some more complicated reactions this relationship may also exist, *but it is not a universal one.* Only experimentation can establish the exponents of the concentrations of the reactants in the rate law and they *may or may not* be the same as the coefficients in the balanced chemical equation.

An explanation for the dependence of the rate on the concentrations of reactants lies in the *Collision Theory of Reaction Rates.* For bimolecular reactions, the rate is proportional to the frequency of collisions between reacting molecules; i.e., to the number of collisions per unit time. As we shall see later, only a small fraction of the collisions result in reaction, but the greater the opportunity for collision the greater the rate of reaction. Thus an increase in either the concentration of hydrogen or of iodine gases in the example discussed above, the greater will be the rate of reaction. Since pressure is directly proportional to the number of molecules per unit volume of gas, an increase in pressure will have the same effect as an increase in concentration.

2   Effect of Temperature

The fact that temperature has an effect on rates of reaction was established very early. By 1889 Arrhenius pointed out that the negative logarithm of the specific reaction rate constant is inversely proportional to the absolute temperature. Mathematically, this can be expressed as

$$\log k = \log A - \frac{E^\ddagger}{2.303RT} \qquad \text{2-3}$$

or in the exponential form known as the Arrhenius equation

$$k = Ae^{-E^\ddagger/RT} \qquad \text{2-4}$$

where k is the specific reaction rate constant, A is a temperature-independent constant of integration, $E^{\ddagger}$ is the Arrhenius activation energy, R is the molar gas constant 1.987 cal/(mole-°K), and T is the Kelvin temperature.

One might wonder why every collision between molecules does not result in reaction. There are several reasons. First, for a reaction to occur between a molecule of hydrogen and a molecule of iodine, the molecules must come together in a favorable configuration for an H-H bond and an I-I bond to be broken, followed by formation of two H-I bonds. If the collisions do not result in favorable configurations, the molecules simply rebound without reaction. In Figure 2-1,

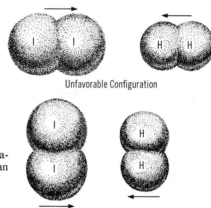

Unfavorable Configuration

Figure 2-1 Two possible configurations of a hydrogen molecule and an iodine molecule on collision.

Favorable Configuration

two possible configurations are represented, but many others are also possible. The constant A (see Eq. 2-3) is related in part to the probability that molecules will collide in an orientation favorable to reaction.

Second, even in a favorable configuration, there is an increase in potential energy as the molecules move close together because of the repulsion of electron clouds of the two molecules as shown by the potential energy diagram in Figure 2-2. The Arrhenius activation energy can be regarded as the minimum energy required to bring the reactants together in an "intermediate configuration" such that either reactants or products can form when the intermediate decomposes. Such an intermediate is called the *activated complex*. Only in those collisions where the relative kinetic energies of the molecules are equal to, or greater than, the activation energy can there be any chance of

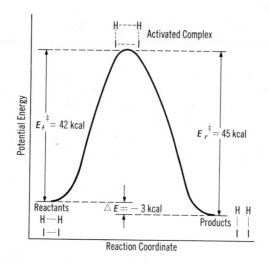

Figure 2-2 Representation of the potential energy change during the reaction $H_2(g) + I_2(g) \rightarrow 2HI(g)$; $E_f^{\ddagger}$ represents the activation energy for the forward reaction; $E_r^{\ddagger}$ represents the activation energy for the reverse reaction; ΔE represents the energy change for the formation of hydrogen iodide from the elements at constant volume and temperature.

reaction. Only such collisions will allow the reactants to form the activated complex.

The energy required to form the activated complex may be determined by making a plot of the logarithm of the specific reaction rate constant *vs.* the reciprocal of the absolute temperature, i.e., log k *vs.* $1/T$. The slope of such a plot is $-E^{\ddagger}/2.303R$. The activation energy may also be obtained from the equation

$$\log \frac{k_2}{k_1} = \frac{E^{\ddagger}}{2.303R}\left(\frac{1}{T_1} - \frac{1}{T_2}\right) \qquad \textbf{2-5}$$

where k_1 and k_2 are the specific reaction rate constants at temperatures T_1 and T_2, respectively. For the formation of hydrogen iodide from the elements, Taylor and Crist [*J. Am. Chem. Soc.*, **63**, 1377 (1941)] found k to be 67.0 M^{-1}-sec^{-1} at 698.6°K and 15.59 M^{-1}-sec^{-1} at 666.8°K. By substitution in Eq. 2-5, we obtain the relation

$$\log \frac{67.0}{15.59} = \frac{E_f^{\ddagger}}{2.303 \times 1.987}\left(\frac{1}{666.8} - \frac{1}{698.6}\right) \qquad \textbf{2-6}$$

On solving, one finds that $E_f^{\ddagger} = 42,000$ cal. This is the energy required to form the activated complex shown in Figure 2-2. For the decomposition of hydrogen iodide, k is 1.242 M^{-1}-sec^{-1} at 698.6°K and

0.259 M^{-1}-sec^{-1} at 666.8°K; $E_r^{\ddagger}$ for the reverse reaction is calculated to be 45,000 cal.

Third, not all molecules in a gas at a given temperature have the same energy and it often happens that only the most energetic molecules have enough energy to react. The fraction of molecules having more than a particular amount of energy is given by the approximate form of the Boltzman distribution function

$$\frac{n_i}{n_t} = \frac{2}{\sqrt{\pi}} \left(\frac{E_i}{RT}\right)^{1/2} e^{-E_i/RT} \qquad \textbf{2-7}$$

where n_i is the number of the molecules having energy greater than E_i and n_t is the total number of molecules.

It has been observed experimentally that, as the temperature rises, the rate of reaction increases more rapidly than the increase in the number of collisions between molecules. This must mean that a higher fraction of collisions result in reaction at elevated temperatures. The fraction of molecules having a sufficient energy to form the activated complex increases more rapidly than the collision frequency. For the formation of hydrogen iodide, the activation energy is 42 kcal. At 666.8°K, only $3.0 \times 10^{-12}\%$ of the molecules have an energy equal to or greater than the minimum required to form the activated complex. At 698°K $4.5 \times 10^{-11}\%$ have sufficient energy to react. This means that 15 times as many molecules have the necessary energy to form the activated complex at the higher temperature than at the lower temperature.

It should also be noted that the difference of the activation energies of the forward and reverse reactions is equal to the energy change for the net chemical reaction at constant volume and temperature. Thus

$$\Delta E = E_f^{\ddagger} - E_r^{\ddagger} \qquad \textbf{2-8}$$

For the formation of hydrogen iodide from the elements, $E_f^{\ddagger} = 42$ kcal and for the reverse reaction $E_r^{\ddagger} = 45$ kcal. Therefore

$$\Delta E = 42 - 45 = -3 \text{ kcal}$$

3   Effect of a Catalyst

A catalyst offers an alternate path by which the chemical reaction may occur. The activation energy for the reaction by the alternative path may be greater or less than the path which does not involve the catalyst. If the activation energy is significantly greater, there will be little effect on the observed overall rate and the material added appears to have no catalytic effect. If the activation energy by the new path is much less, then, for a comparable set of conditions, the reaction will proceed much more rapidly because a higher fraction of the molecules will now have the necessary activation energy. It sometimes happens that the activation energies for two paths are comparable and in those instances the reaction will occur by both paths.

2–B   EQUILIBRIUM CONSTANTS FROM REACTION RATES

The law describing the rate of a given chemical reaction *must be determined experimentally*. As mentioned previously, a close relationship exists between the coefficients in the chemical equation and the exponents of the concentrations in the rate law. For others, there is no obvious correlation. For the reaction represented by the equation

$$H_2(g) + I_2(g) \xrightarrow{\ k_9\ } 2\,HI(g) \qquad \textbf{2-9}$$

the exponents of the concentrations in the rate law have been found to correspond exactly with the coefficients in the chemical equation. The rate of formation (R_9) of hydrogen iodide is given by the equation*

$$R_9 = k_9[H_2][I_2] \qquad \textbf{2-10}$$

where k_9 is the specific reaction rate constant for the forward reaction and $[H_2]$ and $[I_2]$ are the molar concentrations. Similarly, the decomposition of hydrogen iodide is a second order reaction shown by the equation

$$2\,HI(g) \xrightarrow{\ k_{-9}\ } H_2(g) + I_2(g) \qquad \textbf{2-11}$$

The rate is proportional to the square of the concentration of hydrogen iodide gas

$$R_{-9} = k_{-9}[HI]^2 \qquad \textbf{2-12}$$

where k_{-9} is the specific reaction rate constant for the reverse reaction. The exponent here also corresponds to the coefficient of hydrogen iodide in the balanced equation. This is always true for a reaction occurring in a single reversible step or elementary process.

---

* The sum of the exponents of the concentrations in the rate equation gives the *order* of the reaction. The formation of hydrogen iodide is therefore a second order reaction.

Figure 2-3 shows how the concentration of hydrogen, iodine and hydrogen iodide change with time. Figure 2-4 shows a plot of the reaction rates of both the forward and reverse reactions as a function

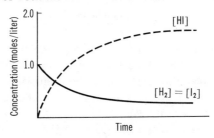

Figure 2-3 Decrease in concentration of $H_2(g)$ and $I_2(g)$ and increase in concentration of $HI(g)$ *vs.* time.

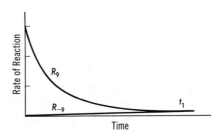

Figure 2-4 Rate of reaction for formation (R_9) and decomposition (R_{-9}) of $HI(g)$ *vs.* time for concentrations in Figure 2-3. Time axis is the same for Figures 2-3 and 2-4.

of time. When equilibrium is established, the forward and reverse rates are equal and

$$k_9[H_2][I_2] = k_{-9}[HI]^2 \qquad \textbf{2-13}$$

Solving for the ratio of k_9/k_{-9}

$$\frac{k_9}{k_{-9}} = \frac{[HI]^2}{[H_2][I_2]} \qquad \textbf{2-14}$$

Since k_9/k_{-9} is a ratio of two numerical constants, it can be replaced by a single constant K_c, called the *equilibrium constant*

$$K_c = \frac{[HI]^2}{[H_2][I_2]} \qquad \textbf{2-15}$$

The result is the equilibrium constant expression for the reversible reaction shown by the equation

$$H_2(g) + I_2(g) \underset{k_{-9}}{\overset{k_9}{\rightleftharpoons}} 2\,HI(g) \qquad \textbf{2-16}$$

9

Taylor and Crist have determined numerical values of k_9 and k_{-9} to be 15.6 and 0.259/(M-sec), respectively, at 666.8°K. At this temperature, the numerical value of K_c is

$$K_c = \frac{k_9}{k_{-9}} = \frac{15.6/(M\text{-sec})}{0.259/(M\text{-sec})} = 60.2 \qquad \textbf{2-17}$$

When reactions occur in more than one step the validity of the derivation of the equilibrium constant expression from kinetics is not obvious. While it is always true that the coefficients in the overall stoichiometric equation are used as exponents in the equilibrium constant expression, *it does not follow that these coefficients are always used as exponents in the rate expression.* Consider the two following kinetically more complicated reactions. Experimentally, it has been found that the reaction

$$2\,NO(g) + O_2(g) \xrightarrow{\ k_{18}\ } 2\,NO_2(g) \qquad \textbf{2-18}$$

is a third order reaction with the rate of the forward reaction being given by the expression

$$R_{18} = k_{18}[NO]^2[O_2] \qquad \textbf{2-19}$$

It is extremely unlikely that 3 molecules will come together in a one step elementary process. A sequence of two reactions which yields the same final products can be shown statistically to be much more probable. This is exemplified by the sequence

$$2\,NO(g) \underset{k_{-20}}{\overset{\overset{\text{fast}}{k_{20}}}{\rightleftharpoons}} N_2O_2(g) \qquad \textbf{2-20}$$

$$N_2O_2(g) + O_2(g) \underset{k_{-21}}{\overset{\overset{\text{slow}}{k_{21}}}{\rightleftharpoons}} 2\,NO_2(g) \qquad \textbf{2-21}$$

where the production of N_2O_2 by the reaction shown in Eq. 2-20 occurs very rapidly compared to the final step shown in Eq. 2-21. The sum of the two consecutive reactions gives the overall reaction shown by the equation

$$2\,NO(g) + O_2(g) \rightleftharpoons 2\,NO_2(g) \qquad \textbf{2-22}$$

At equilibrium

$$R_{20} = k_{20}[NO]^2 = R_{-20} = k_{-20}[N_2O_2] \qquad \textbf{2-23}$$
$$R_{21} = k_{21}[N_2O_2][O_2] = R_{-21} = k_{-21}[NO_2]^2 \qquad \textbf{2-24}$$

For the system to be at true chemical equilibrium, each elementary step or process in the sequence must be at equilibrium. This is sometimes called the *Principle of Microscopic Reversibility.*

Solving for k_{20}/k_{-20} and k_{21}/k_{-21}

$$\frac{k_{20}}{k_{-20}} = \frac{[N_2O_2]}{[NO]^2} \quad \text{and} \quad \frac{k_{21}}{k_{-21}} = \frac{[NO_2]^2}{[N_2O_2][O_2]} \qquad \textbf{2-25}$$

The equilibrium constant for the overall reaction shown in Eq. 2-22 is obtained by eliminating the concentration of the intermediate, N_2O_2, between the two equations. If this is done, the relation obtained is

$$\frac{k_{20}k_{21}}{k_{-20}k_{-21}} = \frac{[NO_2]^2}{[NO]^2[O_2]} = K_c \qquad \textbf{2-26}$$

For the reaction represented by 2-22, the exponents in the final equilibrium constant expression (2-26) happen to be the same as those in rate expression (2-19).

An alternative sequence of reactions for the overall reaction shown by Eq. 2-22 might be given as

$$NO(g) + O_2(g) \overset{\text{fast}}{\rightleftharpoons} NO_3(g) \qquad \textbf{2-27a}$$

$$\underline{NO_3(g) + NO(g) \overset{\text{slow}}{\rightleftharpoons} 2\,NO_2(g)} \qquad \textbf{2-27b}$$

$$2\,NO(g) + O_2(g) \rightleftharpoons 2\,NO_2(g) \qquad \textbf{2-27}$$

Obviously this sequence of reactions would lead to the same equilibrium constant expression for K_c. If the reaction occurs by both paths, the Principle of Microscopic Reversibility requires that each elementary step of each path be at equilibrium when the system as a whole is at equilibrium.

As mentioned earlier, it sometimes happens that for complicated reactions, the exponents of the concentrations in the rate equations do *not* correspond to the exponents in the equilibrium constant expression or to the coefficients of the formulas in the balanced chemical equation. For the reaction

$$2\,NO_2(g) + F_2(g) \rightleftharpoons 2\,NO_2F(g) \qquad \textbf{2-28}$$

the rate expression is

$$R_{28} = k_{28}[NO_2][F_2] \qquad \textbf{2-29}$$

Note that the concentration of NO_2 is raised to the first power rather than the second as might be anticipated from the chemical equation. If only the rate expression, Eq. 2-29, is used for the forward reaction, an erroneous expression for the equilibrium constant results. However, if the reaction is envisioned as occurring by a sequence of elementary reversible processes, then the correct equilibrium constant expression can be deduced. A plausible explanation of the observed rate can be made with the following sequence

$$NO_2(g) + F_2(g) \underset{}{\overset{slow}{\rightleftharpoons}} NO_2F(g) + F(g) \qquad \textbf{2-30}$$

$$F(g) + NO_2(g) \underset{}{\overset{fast}{\rightleftharpoons}} NO_2F(g) \qquad \textbf{2-31}$$

At equilibrium

$$R_{30} = k_{30}[NO_2][F_2] = R_{-30} = k_{-30}[NO_2F][F] \qquad \textbf{2-32}$$
$$R_{31} = k_{31}[F][NO_2] = R_{-31} = k_{-31}[NO_2F] \qquad \textbf{2-33}$$

Again, each individual elementary process must be in equilibrium in an equilibrated system, and the relationships above must hold. Eliminating the concentration of the unstable intermediate gaseous fluorine atoms from the two expressions above

$$[F] = \frac{k_{30}[NO_2][F_2]}{k_{-30}[NO_2F]} = \frac{k_{-31}[NO_2F]}{k_{31}[NO_2]} \qquad \textbf{2-34}$$

Collecting constant terms on the left

$$\frac{k_{30}k_{31}}{k_{-30}k_{-31}} = \frac{[NO_2F]^2}{[NO_2]^2[F_2]} = K_c \qquad \textbf{2-35}$$

This expression for K_c has the correct form for the equilibrium constant for the overall reaction, Eq. 2-28.

Numerous cases of still more complicated rate expressions are known. By the expedient of separating the overall process into a sequence of elementary processes or reversible steps, it is possible to reconcile the equilibrium constant expression with the reaction rate expression. For the equilibrium reaction represented by the equation

$$a\,A + b\,B \rightleftharpoons c\,C + d\,D \qquad \textbf{2-36}$$

a, b, c, and d are the coefficients of substances A, B, C, and D in the balanced chemical equation. When the system reaches a state of equilibrium, the concentrations of the reactants and products no longer change with time. They are then related by the expression

$$K_c = \frac{[C]^c[D]^d}{[A]^a[B]^b} \qquad \textbf{2-37}$$

This relationship may also be derived from the principles of chemical thermodynamics as will be shown in Chapter 3.

Recent experiments by Dr. J. H. Sullivan (*J. Chem. Phys.*, **46**, 73 (1967)) have shown that the reaction of hydrogen and iodine gases may be more complicated than scientists until now have believed. He has shown that at temperatures between 418 and 520°K, the reaction occurs in two steps

$$\text{Step 1: } I_2(g) \rightarrow 2I(g)$$
$$\text{Step 2: } 2I(g) + H_2(g) \rightarrow 2HI(g)$$

Complete reaction: $H_2(g) + I_2(g) \rightarrow 2HI(g)$

At the higher temperatures at which the investigations of Taylor and Crist were carried out, the two mechanisms are kinetically indistinguishable because iodine molecules rapidly establish equilibrium with iodine atoms. This causes the rate equation for both mechanisms to have the same dependence on iodine concentration. Dr. Sullivan presents arguments which make the two step reaction seem highly probable over the temperature range of both investigations. The equilibrium constant expression as we have discussed it is independent of the mechanism of the reaction.

2–C FACTORS INFLUENCING THE EQUILIBRIUM STATE OF THE SYSTEM

1 Effect of Time

For a system in a state of stable equilibrium at constant temperature and pressure, the system is in its lowest energy state and no changes take place with the passage of time. This is another way of saying that once equilibrium has been established, the rates of the various processes are constant because the concentrations of all species present in the system have achieved steady state values. This is illustrated graphically in Figure 2-4. It is also evident from Figure 2-4 that at any point in time after t_1, when the rates R_9 and R_{-9} become the same, the system is considered to be in an equilibrium state.

To determine the equilibrium constant for a reaction such as that given by the equation

$$H_2(g) + I_2(g) \rightleftharpoons 2\,HI(g) \qquad \qquad \textbf{2-38}$$

known numbers of moles of hydrogen and iodine are allowed to react until equilibrium is established. Then a determination is made of how much hydrogen iodide has been produced and how much hydrogen and iodine are unreacted. Since both the forward and reverse reactions are slow at room temperature, a sample equilibrated at an elevated temperature may be "quenched" by lowering the temperature suddenly. The composition of the mixture is still the same as at the elevated temperature. If a chemical analysis is now carried out for iodine and/or hydrogen iodide before any change in the relative amounts of the two has occurred, then the concentrations or pressures of the substances in the equilibrium mixture at the elevated temperatures may be calculated. In one experiment, Taylor and Crist prepared a flask containing 1.121×10^{-2} mole of hydrogen per liter and 9.24×10^{-3} mole of iodine per liter. After allowing the sample to stand at $666.8°K$ for 1860 minutes for equilibrium to be established, they quenched the reaction mixture and found on analysis that the concentration of iodine which remained was 1.29×10^{-3} mole per liter. With this information they calculated the equilibrium concentrations of the three species to be as follows:

$$[H_2] = 3.26 \times 10^{-3}M$$
$$[I_2] = 1.29 \times 10^{-3}M$$
$$[HI] = 1.59 \times 10^{-2}M$$

By substituting these numbers into the equilibrium constant expression for the chemical reaction the numerical value of K_c may be obtained.

$$K_c = \frac{[HI]^2}{[H_2][I_2]} \qquad \text{2-39}$$

$$K_c = \frac{(1.59 \times 10^{-2}M)^2}{(3.26 \times 10^{-3}M)(1.29 \times 10^{-2}M)}$$

$$K_c = \frac{2.53 \times 10^{-4}}{4.21 \times 10^{-5}} = 60.1$$

This value of K_c derived from measurements of equilibrium concentrations is almost identical with the value 60.2 obtained from kinetic measurements (see Eq. 2-17).

2   Effect of Concentration

An increase in the concentration of a reactant (or product) in a system which is in chemical equilibrium will cause an unbalance in the rates of the forward and reverse reactions. For the equilibrium shown by Eq. 2-16, an increase in the concentration of hydrogen in the equilibrium mixture at time t_2 causes a sudden increase in the rate of the forward reaction as shown in Figure 2-5. As the concentration of hydrogen iodide builds up, the rate of the reverse reaction also increases while the rate of the forward reaction decreases; eventually the two rates again become equal at time t_3. After equilibrium is re-established, both the forward and reverse rates are higher than they

14

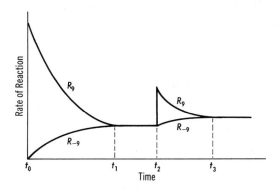

Figure 2-5   A schematic representation of the rate of reaction of H_2 and I_2 to form HI. At t_0, $H_2(g)$ and $I_2(g)$ are mixed, and the rate of the forward reaction is at a maximum. Equilibrium is established at time t_1. Additional H_2 is introduced at t_2 and the rate of the forward reaction increases suddenly. At time t_3, the rates of the forward and reverse reactions are again equal and equilibrium is re-established.

were at t_1. The concentrations of hydrogen and hydrogen iodide are greater at t_3 than at t_1, and the concentration of iodine is reduced by an amount which equals one-half the increase in concentration of hydrogen iodide.

This behavior is described qualitatively by Le Chatelier's principle: *"When a change is made in any of the factors determining the state of an equilibrium system, a process will occur to minimize the imposed change."* This principle predicts that when the hydrogen iodide system just discussed is disturbed by the addition of hydrogen at constant volume, a reaction occurs which uses up some of the added hydrogen. The only reaction which can accomplish this is the conversion of hydrogen and iodine to hydrogen iodide.

Let us now see what quantitative changes occur when hydrogen gas is added to a hydrogen, iodine, and hydrogen iodide equilibrium system. Assume that 5.00×10^{-3} mole of hydrogen gas are added to 1 liter of the equilibrium mixture described in Section 2-B, following Eq. 2-38. After a period corresponding to the time difference between t_3 and t_2 in Figure 2-5, equilibrium is re-established and a new set of equilibrium concentrations exists. What are these concentrations?

Let $X =$ the decrease in the concentration of iodine gas. Then $2X =$ the increase in concentration of hydrogen iodide caused by the reaction, because one mole of H_2 reacts with 1 mole of I_2 to yield

15

2 moles of HI. The new equilibrium concentrations are

[HI] = [old equilibrium concentration + amount formed]

[H₂] = [old concentration + amount added − amount reacted]

[I₂] = [old concentration − amount reacted]

$[HI] = (1.59 \times 10^{-2} + 2X)M$

$[H_2] = (3.26 \times 10^{-3} + 5.00 \times 10^{-3} - X) = (8.26 \times 10^{-3} - X)M$

$[I_2] = (1.29 \times 10^{-3} - X)M$

Substituting these numbers in the equilibrium constant expression and using the numerical value 60.1 for K_c

$$60.1 = \frac{(1.59 \times 10^{-2} + 2X)^2}{(8.26 \times 10^{-3} - X)(1.29 \times 10^{-3} - X)}$$

$$X = 6.45 \times 10^{-4}M$$

The new equilibrium concentrations are

$$[HI] = 1.72 \times 10^{-2}M$$
$$[H_2] = 7.62 \times 10^{-3}M$$
$$[I_2] = 6.5 \times 10^{-4}M$$

Compared to the concentrations at the old equilibrium, these have changed in the direction predicted by Le Chatelier's principle.

3   Effect of Pressure

It should be clearly noted at the outset that a change in the pressure of one component of an equilibrium mixture may produce a different effect from changing the total pressure on the system. Addition or removal of some number of moles of one substance at constant volume changes the partial pressure of that component to a much greater extent than it changes the total pressure of the system. The result is quite different from that obtained by changing the total pressure by increasing or decreasing the volume of the system.

From the ideal gas equation $p_i = (n_i/V)RT$, the pressure p_i of a given gas is directly proportional to the number of moles (or molecules) of that gas per unit volume. Hence, changing the pressure of a single component of a system in chemical equilibrium has the same effect as changing its concentration. Increasing the pressure increases the opportunity for collisions between molecules. The arguments presented in the preceding section relative to concentration changes apply equally well to pressure changes caused by the addition or removal of a single gaseous component at constant volume.

To predict the effects of changes in total pressure on a system in equilibrium, we should first recognize that it is possible and often convenient to express the equilibrium constant for a gaseous reaction in terms of pressures rather than concentrations. Several reactions and their corresponding equilibrium constant expressions are

$$H_2(g) + I_2(g) \rightleftharpoons 2\,HI(g) \qquad \text{2-40}$$

$$K_p = \frac{(p_{HI})^2}{(p_{H_2})(p_{I_2})} \qquad \text{2-41}$$

$$N_2F_4(g) \rightleftharpoons 2\,NF_2(g) \qquad \text{2-42}$$

$$K_p = \frac{(p_{NF_2})^2}{(p_{N_2F_4})} \qquad \text{2-43}$$

$$N_2(g) + 3\,H_2(g) \rightleftharpoons 2\,NH_3(g) \qquad \text{2-44}$$

$$K_p = \frac{(p_{NH_3})^2}{(p_{N_2})(p_{H_2})^3} \qquad \text{2-45}$$

Le Chatelier's principle provides a simple means of determining the effect of a change in total pressure on a system in a state of chemical equilibrium. Consider a gas enclosed in a cylinder fitted with a piston. When the pressure exerted by the piston is increased at constant temperature, the volume occupied by the gas is thereby decreased. Le Chatelier's principle predicts a chemical change will occur which tends to reduce the increased pressure. This can occur only if the reaction proceeds in such a way as to reduce the total number of molecules per unit volume. For the N_2F_4 dissociation (Eq. 2-42), an increase in pressure causes NF_2 to re-combine to form N_2F_4. This is because fewer molecules exist in the system when the components are in the form of N_2F_4 than when they exist as NF_2. For the NH_3 equilibrium (Eq. 2-44), an increase in pressure favors NH_3 formation because this decreases the number of molecules. In the case of the hydrogen iodide equilibrium (Eq. 2-40), a change in total pressure does not change the ratio of reactants to products because the number of molecules of products formed equals the number of molecules of reactants consumed.

To have a more quantitative approach to determine the effect of changing the total pressure of an equilibrium system, one must obtain a mathematical relationship between the extent to which a reaction has occurred and the total pressure of a system. This can be achieved through the equilibrium constant expression. Let us again consider the dissociation shown by the equation

$$N_2F_4(g) \rightleftharpoons 2\,NF_2(g) \qquad \text{2-46}$$

for which

$$K_p = \frac{(p_{NF_2})^2}{p_{N_2F_4}} \qquad \text{2-47}$$

Let n = the total number of moles of N_2F_4 originally added to a flask of known volume at a certain temperature.

         α = the fraction of the total moles of N_2F_4 which have dissociated when equilibrium is established. α is sometimes called the degree of dissociation.

    $(1 - \alpha)$ = the fraction of the total moles of N_2F_4 remaining undissociated.

At equilibrium:

P_t = total pressure of the system $= p_{NF_2} + p_{N_2F_4}$ **2-48**

Number of moles of N_2F_4 $= (1 - \alpha)n$

Number of moles of NF_2 $= (2\alpha)n$

Total number of moles of both
components at equilibrium $= n_{eq} = (1 + \alpha)n$ **2-49**

Mole fraction of $N_2F_4 = X_1 = \dfrac{(1 - \alpha)n}{(1 + \alpha)n} = \dfrac{(1 - \alpha)}{(1 + \alpha)}$

Mole fraction of $NF_2 = X_2 = \dfrac{2\alpha n}{(1 + \alpha)n} = \dfrac{2\alpha}{1 + \alpha}$

Since the total pressure on the system is P_t, then

$$p_{N_2F_4} = X_1 P_t = \left(\frac{1 - \alpha}{1 + \alpha}\right)P_t \qquad \textbf{2-50}$$

$$p_{NF_2} = X_2 P_t = \left(\frac{2\alpha}{1 + \alpha}\right)P_t \qquad \textbf{2-51}$$

Substituting into the expression for K_p

$$K_p = \frac{\left(\dfrac{2\alpha P_t}{1 + \alpha}\right)^2}{\dfrac{(1 - \alpha)P_t}{1 + \alpha}} = \frac{4\alpha^2 P_t}{(1 - \alpha^2)} \qquad \textbf{2-52}$$

This equation expresses the relationship between the degree of dissociation α and the total pressure P_t. As P_t increases, $\alpha^2/(1 - \alpha^2)$ must decrease because K_p must remain constant. The value of the fraction $\alpha^2/(1 - \alpha^2)$ decreases when α approaches zero, i.e., as the partial pressure of N_2F_4 increases. Stated differently, as P_t increases (by decreasing the volume of the container), α decreases. Similarly, if P_t is decreased, then $\alpha^2/(1 - \alpha^2)$ must increase; this occurs as α approaches unity.

When a chemical reaction occurs at constant volume and temperature, there will be a change in the total pressure of the system if the sum of the moles of gaseous products is different from the sum of the moles of gaseous reactants. Since a reversible chemical reaction proceeds until equilibrium is established, a measurement of the equilibrium pressure will be a measure of the extent of reaction and will allow the calculation of the equilibrium constant. A sample calculation follows. A 0.570 g sample of $N_2F_4(g)$ was placed in a 1.000 liter flask and heated to a temperature of 423°K. When equilibrium was established the total pressure was determined to be 0.224 atm. From the ideal gas equation, the number of moles of gas at equilibrium was calculated.

$$n_{eq} = PV/RT = (0.224 \times 1.000)/(0.0821 \times 423) = 6.45 \times 10^{-3} \text{ mole}$$

The original number of moles of undissociated N_2F_4 may be calculated by dividing the mass of the sample by its molecular weight. Therefore

$$n = \frac{0.570 \text{ g}}{104.0 \text{ g/mole}} = 5.48 \times 10^{-3} \text{ mole}$$

On substitution of n and n_{eq} in Eq. 2-49, α may be obtained

$$\alpha = \frac{n_{eq}}{n} - 1 = \frac{6.45 \times 10^{-3}}{5.48 \times 10^{-3}} - 1 = 0.177$$

Substituting the values of α and P_t in Eq. 2-52, we obtain

$$K_p = \frac{4(0.177)^2(0.224)}{[1 - (0.177)^2]} = 2.90 \times 10^{-2} \text{ atm}$$

Other values of α have been determined in a similar fashion for $N_2F_4(g)$ at 423°K, and these data are plotted in Figure 2-6. It should be observed from this figure that as the total pressure is decreased from 0.720 atm to 0.224 atm, the degree of dissociation increases from 0.100 to 0.177. Because of this change in total applied pressure, the extent of reaction increases from 10.0% to 17.7%.

To illustrate that K_p is in fact constant, we shall calculate K_p for the other set of data presented in the preceding paragraph. When the total pressure was 0.720 atm, $\alpha = 0.100$.

$$K_p = \frac{4(0.100)^2(0.720)}{1.000 - (0.100)^2} = 2.91 \times 10^{-2} \text{ atm}$$

Within the limits of error of the data presented, it is observed that K_p is constant.

In a similar way, the extent to which a stoichiometric mixture of nitrogen and hydrogen has reacted may be expressed as a function of the equilibrium constant and the total pressure of the system. Figure 2-6 shows a plot of this function for ammonia formation. Figure 2-6

19

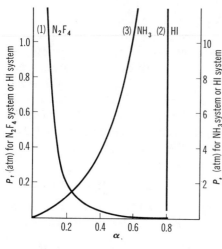

Figure 2-6 Variation of the extent of reaction, α, as a function of total pressure, P_t. (1) N_2F_4 dissociation at 423°K. (2) HI formation from a stoichiometric mixture of H_2 and I_2 (1:1) at 666.8°K. (3) NH_3 formation from a stoichiometric mixture of H_2 and N_2 (3:1) at 500°K.

also shows that the extent to which a stoichiometric mixture of hydrogen and iodine reacts is independent of the total pressure; that is, the equilibrium constant expression does not include a term in P_t. The behavior predicted earlier for the effect of pressure on these systems is easily seen from these plots.

4 Effect of a Catalyst

The presence of a catalyst in a system at chemical equilibrium does not affect the concentrations of the reactants or those of the products. The addition of a catalyst to a system which is not at equilibrium may provide an alternative path whereby the chemical reaction can proceed faster, and as a result the equilibrium state is attained more rapidly than in the absence of the catalyst. However, the principle of microscopic reversibility requires that the rate of the reverse reaction also be increased. When equilibrium is established, the concentrations of reactants and products are the same as they would have been if equilibrium were established in the absence of the catalyst. In Figure 2-7 this behavior of a catalyst is presented schematically.

5 Effect of Temperature on a System in Chemical Equilibrium

Chemical reactions are classified as endothermic or exothermic. In the former heat is absorbed from the surroundings, and in the latter heat is liberated to the surroundings. For a closed system at constant temperature and pressure, this heat change is known as the enthalpy change, ΔH, for the reaction. ΔH is positive for an endothermic

20

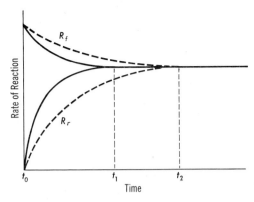

Figure 2-7 Effect of catalyst on establishment of equilibrium. Equilibrium is established at time t_2 in the absence of a catalyst (dashed curves) and at the time t_1 in the presence of a catalyst (solid curves).

reaction and negative for an exothermic reaction; usually it is expressed in either calories or kilocalories.

For a given chemical reaction, ΔH is the enthalpy change when that number of moles of reactants shown by the balanced chemical equation reacts to form the products. Enthalpy changes are commonly represented in general chemistry textbooks in two different ways. One way is to include the enthalpy change as an integral part of the equation which is written

$$H_2(g) + I_2(g) \rightleftharpoons 2\,HI(g) - \Delta H \qquad \textbf{2-53}$$

This reaction is exothermic with $\Delta H = -3$ kcal, and the equation is sometimes written as

$$H_2(g) + I_2(g) \rightleftharpoons 2\,HI(g) + 3 \text{ kcal} \qquad \textbf{2-54}$$

The equation for the endothermic decomposition of N_2F_4 is written as

$$N_2F_4(g) \rightleftharpoons 2\,NF_2(g) - 19.5 \text{ kcal} \qquad \textbf{2-55}$$

This equation may also be written

$$N_2F_4(g) + 19.5 \text{ kcal} \rightleftharpoons 2\,NF_2(g) \qquad \textbf{2-56}$$

In the second notation the enthalpy changes may be shown as

$$H_2(g) + I_2(g) \rightleftharpoons 2\,HI(g) \qquad \Delta H = -3 \text{ kcal} \qquad \textbf{2-57}$$

$$N_2F_4(g) \rightleftharpoons 2\,NF_2(g) \qquad \Delta H = +19.5 \text{ kcal} \qquad \textbf{2-58}$$

When the temperature of a system in a state of chemical equilibrium is raised, both the rates of the forward and the reverse reactions

21

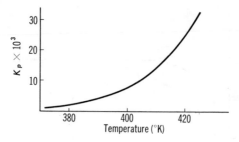

Figure 2-8 Variation in K_p for the endothermic reaction $N_2F_4(g) \rightleftharpoons 2\,NF_2(g)$ as a function of temperature.

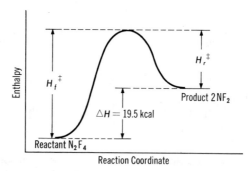

Figure 2-9 Schematic activation enthalpy plot for N_2F_4 dissociation.

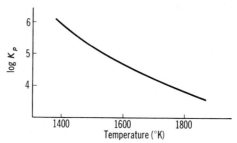

Figure 2-10 Change in $\log K_p$ for the exothermic reaction $CO(g) + 1/2\,O_2(g) \rightleftharpoons CO_2(g)$ as a function of temperature.

increase and a chemical reaction occurs until a new equilibrium state is established. Experiments have shown that for endothermic reactions, an increase in the numerical value of the equilibrium constant accompanies an increase in temperature. The dissociation of N_2F_4 is endothermic, and Figure 2-8 shows a plot of K_p vs. T for this reaction. If the temperature of an equilibrium system containing N_2F_4 is increased, N_2F_4 molecules absorb heat and dissociate. Thus a higher

22

fraction of the molecules exist in the form of NF_2 at the higher temperature. Such behavior is in accord with Le Chatelier's principle, which predicts that when the temperature of an equilibrium system is increased, that chemical reaction will occur which absorbs heat, thereby tending to *minimize* the increase in temperature. From the activation enthalpy plot in Figure 2-9 for the dissociation of N_2F_4, it is seen that when reactant molecules are excited enough to form the activated complex, more heat is absorbed than when product molecules form the same activated complex. From this point of view, Le Chatelier's principle would again predict that this reaction should proceed toward completion as the temperature is increased. This means that the rate constant of the forward reaction increases proportionately more with increasing temperature than does that of the reverse reaction.

The opposite behavior is observed for exothermic reactions wherein a decrease in equilibrium constant accompanies an increase in temperature as shown in Figure 2-10. For the formation of carbon dioxide from carbon monoxide and oxygen at 1500°K

$$CO(g) + 1/2\ O_2(g) \rightleftharpoons CO_2(g) \qquad \Delta H = -66.5\ \text{kcal} \qquad \textbf{2-59}$$

or

$$CO(g) + 1/2\ O_2(g) \rightleftharpoons CO_2(g) + 66.5\ \text{kcal} \qquad \textbf{2-60}$$

An increase in temperature changes one of the factors which determines the equilibrium state of the system, and to minimize the temperature increase, a reaction occurs which absorbs heat. That is, carbon dioxide absorbs heat and dissociates as the temperature is increased. In this instance, the rate constant of the reverse reaction increases proportionately more with increasing temperature than does that of the forward reaction.

Problems   (*Answers to problems are on page 114–115.*)

2-1   The reaction $2\ NO(g) \rightarrow N_2(g) + O_2(g)$ is a second order reaction, and the rate expression is $R_f = k[NO]^2$. The rate constant at 962°K is 0.0398 $M^{-1}\text{-sec}^{-1}$, and at 1250°K the constant is 1.074 $M^{-1}\text{-sec}^{-1}$. Determine $E^{\ddagger}$ for the reaction.

2-2   The reaction $CO\ (g) + NO_2(g) \rightarrow CO_2(g) + NO(g)$ occurs at elevated temperatures and is second order. The following data were collected:

Temperature	Rate Constant
540°K	0.0019 $M^{-1}\text{-sec}^{-1}$
592	0.0174
638	0.110
727	1.5

Make a plot of log k *vs.* $1/T$ and determine $E^{\ddagger}$.

23

2-3   For the conversion between the two different structural forms of 1,2-dichloroethene as shown by the equation

$$\text{(cis)} \qquad \text{(trans)},$$

the rate constant for the forward reaction at 185°C is 3.9×10^{-6} sec^{-1}, and that for the reverse reaction is 6.8×10^{-6} sec^{-1}. If both reactions are first order, what is the equilibrium constant for the reaction at 185°C?

2-4   At 1500°K, the equilibrium constant for the reaction $CO_2(g) + H_2(g) \rightleftharpoons CO(g + H_2O(g)$ is 3.05. What fraction of an equimolar mixture of CO_2 and H_2 has reacted when equilibrium is established?

2-5   From vapor density measurements, it has been found that a given sample of $COBr_2(g)$ is 78% dissociated at a total pressure of 3.47 atm and a temperature of 346°K. What are the values of K_p and K_c at this temperature?

2-6   For the reaction shown by the equation $CO(g) + Br_2(g) \rightleftharpoons COBr_2(g)$, $K_p = 0.0475$ atm^{-1} at 454°K. An equimolar mixture of carbon monoxide and bromine is placed in a cylinder fitted with a piston. Make a plot of the fraction of the original material which has reacted *vs.* the total applied pressure when equilibrium is established at a temperature of 454°K.

2-7   The reaction shown by the equation $SO_2(g) + NO_2(g) \rightleftharpoons NO(g) + SO_3(g)$ occurs at elevated temperatures. An equilibrium mixture in a 1.0 liter container is analyzed and the concentrations of NO and SO_3 are found to be 0.29 mole/liter and those of SO_2 and NO_2 are 0.71 mole/liter. What is the equilibrium constant? How many moles of NO_2 would have to be added to the mixture in the one liter container to double the concentration of SO_3.

2-8   For each of the equations below, make a schematic plot of K_p *vs.* T to illustrate the effect of temperature on the equilibrium constant.

$$\begin{aligned}
&Br_2(g) \rightleftharpoons 2\ Br(g) & &\Delta H = +23 \text{ kcal} \\
&2\ CO(g) + O_2(g) \rightleftharpoons 2\ CO_2(g) & &\Delta H = -135 \text{ kcal} \\
&2\ HBr(g) \rightleftharpoons H_2(g) + Br_2(g) & &\Delta H = +17 \text{ kcal} \\
&2\ Cl_2O(g) \rightleftharpoons 2\ Cl_2(g) + O_2(g) & &\Delta H = -36 \text{ kcal}
\end{aligned}$$

24

Thermodynamics of Chemical Reactions

3–A SPONTANEITY AND THE EQUILIBRIUM CONSTANT

Let us now examine some of the material discussed in Chapter 2 to see if there is any information pertinent to the problem of spontaneity; that is, whether a chemical reaction will occur spontaneously. From a consideration of chemical kinetics, we established that the concentrations of chemical species present in a system, not originally in a state of chemical equilibrium, are changed by chemical reaction until the equilibrium constant expression is satisfied. This is a *spontaneous process*. For example, in a nonequilibrium system containing ammonia, hydrogen, and nitrogen, either ammonia will be formed spontaneously by the forward reaction

$$N_2(g) + 3 H_2(g) \rightleftharpoons 2 NH_3(g) \qquad \textbf{3-1}$$

or it will decompose spontaneously by the reverse reaction. When equilibrium is established, the pressures of the various species in the system must satisfy the equilibrium condition

$$K_p = \frac{(p_{NH_3})^2}{(p_{N_2})(p_{H_2})^3} \qquad \textbf{3-2}$$

One criterion for deciding whether a chemical reaction will occur spontaneously depends on a comparison of the existing state of a system and its equilibrium state. The equilibrium condition for any reaction is specified by an equation of the type shown by Eq. 3-2. If the system is at equilibrium, the equilibrium condition is of course met, and no net chemical reaction may occur. If the equilibrium condition is not satisfied, that reaction will occur which allows the system to approach equilibrium. This criterion predicts only that a reaction should occur; it makes no prediction as to how fast the reaction will proceed. To make use of this criterion, we define a function Q which has the same form as the equilibrium constant but which employs the initial arbitrary pressures (or concentrations) at which the reactants and products exist before reaction. Thus for the formation of ammonia by the reaction represented by Eq. 3-1, we obtain

$$Q = \left[\frac{(p_{NH_3})^2}{(p_{N_2})(p_{H_2})^3} \right]_{initial} \qquad \textbf{3-3}$$

If a mixture of nitrogen and hydrogen gases is introduced into a reaction vessel containing no ammonia, the numerical value of Q is equal to zero. Since K_p has a finite value different from zero, the numerator of Eq. 3-3 must somehow be increased. This occurs when ammonia is formed and nitrogen and hydrogen are consumed. The numerical value of Q increases and becomes equal to K_p when equilibrium is established.

Now assume that ammonia gas is introduced into a flask which contains no nitrogen or hydrogen; under these conditions Q has an infinite value. The decomposition of ammonia to nitrogen and hydrogen occurs, causing Q to decrease and approach K_p, and finally at equilibrium become equal to K_p.

The spontaneity of a chemical reaction then rests on the relative numerical values of Q and K_p. If Q is different from K_p a reaction will occur which causes Q to approach K_p. The driving force of a chemical reaction at constant temperature must be related to some function of the difference between Q and K_p.

3–B   SPONTANEITY AND ENTHALPY CHANGES

The enthalpy of a system is a thermodynamic property, and as such, it depends only on the particular state of the system. If the enthalpy of State 1 is H_1 and the enthalpy of State 2 is H_2, then the change in enthalpy on going from State 1 to State 2 is $\Delta H = H_2 - H_1$. ΔH depends only on the initial and final states of the system and is independent of the path by which the change from State 1 to State 2 occurs.

Many reactions occur with the liberation of heat, and early workers such as Thomsen and Berthelot thought that only exothermic reactions

26

could occur spontaneously. Likening a chemical reaction to a ball rolling down hill from a position of high mechanical potential energy to one of lower potential energy, they correctly thought that only those reactions occur which go from a state of high chemical potential energy to one of lower chemical potential energy. Thomsen and Berthelot incorrectly identified chemical potential energy changes with enthalpy changes. In their time (the latter half of the 19th century) it was believed that the criterion of spontaneity or the driving force of a reaction at constant temperature and pressure was its exothermic or endothermic nature. A chemical system reacts to attain the lowest energy state, and the liberation of heat to the surroundings is a manifestation of this reaction. Indeed, many spontaneous chemical reactions are exothermic and many nonspontaneous chemical reactions are highly endothermic. The equations of several such reactions and the enthalpy changes at 298°K are

$$C(s) + O_2(g) \rightarrow CO_2(g) \qquad\qquad \Delta H = -94.1 \text{ kcal}$$

$$2\,CO(g) + O_2(g) \rightarrow 2\,CO_2(g) \qquad \Delta H = -135.3 \text{ kcal}$$

$$4\,Fe(s) + 3\,O_2(g) \rightarrow 2\,Fe_2O_3(s) \qquad \Delta H = -393.6 \text{ kcal}$$

$$H_2(g) + I_2(g) \rightarrow 2\,HI(g) \qquad\qquad \Delta H = -3 \text{ kcal}$$

$$CuO(s) + H_2(g) \rightarrow Cu(s) + H_2O(g) \qquad \Delta H = -20.7 \text{ kcal}$$

$$MgO(s) + H_2(g) \rightarrow Mg(s) + H_2O(g) \qquad \Delta H = +86.0 \text{ kcal}$$

$$Na_2O(s) + H_2(g) \rightarrow 2\,Na(s) + H_2O(g) \qquad \Delta H = +41.6 \text{ kcal}$$

All but the last two reactions occur readily at elevated temperatures with the evolution of heat.

The *heat change is not the only factor* affecting the spontaneity of a reaction taking place at constant temperature and pressure. This is witnessed by the fact that a significant number of chemical reactions that are endothermic do occur spontaneously to an appreciable extent. Some examples are

$$N_2F_4(g) \rightarrow 2\,NF_2(g) \qquad\qquad \Delta H = +19.5 \text{ kcal}$$

$$C(s) + H_2O(g) \rightarrow CO(g) + H_2(g) \qquad \Delta H = +31.4 \text{ kcal}$$

$$2\,NH_3(g) \rightarrow N_2(g) + 3\,H_2(g) \qquad \Delta H = +22.1 \text{ kcal}$$

This set of reactions occurs spontaneously when heat is supplied to the system from the surroundings. Since both exothermic and endothermic reactions may occur spontaneously, the enthalpy change for a system at constant temperature and pressure is *not* in itself a criterion to determine the spontaneity of a chemical reaction.

3–C   SPONTANEITY AND CHEMICAL POTENTIAL (FREE ENERGY)

When a chemical reaction occurs spontaneously at constant temperature and pressure, there is always a *decrease* in a function of the state of the system known as the *chemical potential*, μ, or the Gibbs' *free energy*, G. For a reaction under these conditions, the change of chemical potential may be considered as a change of *chemical potential energy*, or a change of *free energy*. This free energy change, ΔG, equals the sum of the chemical potentials of the products minus the sum of the chemical potentials of the reactants. For a reaction represented by the general equation

$$a\,A + b\,B \rightarrow c\,C + d\,D + e\,E \qquad\qquad \textbf{3-4}$$

where a, b, c, d, and e are the coefficients of the formulas of substances A, B, C, D, and E, respectively. In the balanced chemical equation, the free energy change is given by the equation

$$\Delta G = (c\,\mu_C + d\,\mu_D + e\,\mu_E) - (a\,\mu_A + b\,\mu_B) \qquad\qquad \textbf{3-5}$$

For a spontaneous process to occur at constant temperature and pressure, ΔG must be negative. This condition was first stated by Professor J. Willard Gibbs and corresponds to a change of the system from a state of given chemical potential energy to another having a lower chemical potential energy. This is a way of saying that the total free energy of the products must be less than the total free energy of the reactants. ΔG also represents the maximum possible useful work a system can do when a chemical reaction occurs at constant temperature and pressure.

By methods of chemical thermodynamics, which are, unfortunately, outside the scope of this book, it can be shown that the chemical potential, μ_i, of any gas i at a pressure of p_i is given by the equation

$$\mu_i = \mu^0{}_i + RT \ln p_i/p_i{}^0 \qquad\qquad \textbf{3-6}$$

where $\mu^0{}_i$ is a constant which represents the standard molar chemical potential of a gas when its pressure equals an arbitrarily selected standard pressure $p_i{}^0$. The standard pressure, or standard state, of a gas is usually chosen as a partial pressure of 1 atmosphere. It is seen from Eq. 3-6 that when the standard state is chosen as one atmosphere, and when $p_i = 1$ atmosphere, $\mu_i = \mu^0{}_i$.

The ratio $p_i/p_i{}^0$ for gases behaving ideally is usually called the activity a_i of the gas, or $a_i = p_i/p_i{}^0$. Because the standard state is chosen as 1 atmosphere pressure, a_i is equal to $p_i/1$. Since a_i is the ratio of two pressures, the activity is a unitless quantity.* Eq. 3-6 can also be written as

$$\mu_i = \mu^0_i + RT \ln a_i \qquad \textbf{3-7}$$

In our treatment of equilibrium involving gases, we shall assume that all gases behave ideally and that their activities are numerically equal to their pressures in atmospheres.

For solids and liquids, the chemical potentials are given by an equation similar to Eq. 3-6. Since the activities of solids and liquids are usually stated in terms of their mole fractions, the equation may be written as

$$\mu_i = \mu^0_i + RT \ln X_i/X_i^0 \qquad \textbf{3-8}$$

Here the standard state is usually chosen as the pure substance for which the mole fraction X_i^0 is unity. Hence

$$\mu_i = \mu^0_i + RT \ln X_i \qquad \textbf{3-9}$$

Thus when $X_1 = 1$, then $\mu_i = \mu^0_i$.

Certain conventions have been adopted regarding the assignment of values of μ^0_i. For an *element* in its most stable form at any given temperature at one atmosphere pressure, μ^0_i is assigned the value of zero, but in some other form, μ^0_i is different from zero. For a *compound*, μ^0_i is numerically equal to the standard free energy of formation of the compound, ΔG^0_f. This is the free energy change when the elements in their standard states react to form one mole of the compound in its standard state.

For any chemical reaction where the reactants in their standard states react in the proportion required by the balanced chemical equation to form the products in their standard states, the free energy change, ΔG^0, is the *standard free energy change for the reaction*. For the general reaction illustrated by Eq. 3-4, ΔG^0 is given by the equation

$$\Delta G^0 = (c \, \mu^0_C + d \, \mu^0_D + e \, \mu^0_E) - (a \, \mu^0_A + b \, \mu^0_B) \qquad \textbf{3-10}$$

The *total free energy*, G_t, of any system may be defined as the *sum of the chemical potentials* of all species present. For example

$$G_t = n_a\mu_a + n_b\mu_b + n_c\mu_c + \ldots n_z\mu_z \qquad \textbf{3-11}$$

where n_a, n_b, n_c, ... n_z are the numbers of moles of substances a, b, c, ... z, respectively, which are present in the system. When a chemi-

---

* This causes equilibrium constants calculated using activities to be unitless quantities. These are designated as K^0.

cal reaction occurs, the numbers of moles of some species decrease and the numbers of moles of others increase. There will therefore be changes in the chemical potentials of the individual substances and also of the total free energy of the system. Let us consider in detail these changes in chemical potentials for a simple chemical reaction such as the dissociation of hydrogen iodide

$$2 \, HI(g) \rightleftharpoons I_2(g) + H_2(g) \qquad \text{3-12}$$

As the dissociation proceeds, all three species will be present in the reaction vessel. The total free energy of the system at any point in the reaction is given by the equation

$$G_t = n_{HI}\mu_{HI} + n_{I_2}\mu_{I_2} + n_{H_2}\mu_{H_2} \qquad \text{3-13}$$

Substituting from Eq. 3-7, and taking $p_{HI}{}^0$, $p_{I_2}{}^0$, and $p_{H_2}{}^0$ each to be 1 atm, we obtain the equation

$$G_t = n_{HI}[\mu^0{}_{HI} + RT \ln p_{HI}] + n_{I_2}[\mu^0{}_{I_2} + RT \ln p_{I_2}]$$
$$+ n_{H_2}[\mu^0{}_{H_2} + RT \ln p_{H_2}] \qquad \text{3-14}$$

Suppose we place 2 moles of HI in a flask of sufficient volume so that the pressure of the gas is two atmospheres when the temperature is 666.8°K. Let us now calculate the total free energy of the system corresponding to various degrees of dissociation of hydrogen iodide. Let the fraction of the number of moles of hydrogen iodide present which have dissociated be called the degree of dissociation and be defined by α. By consideration of the balanced Eq. 3-12, the number of moles of the various species are related to α by

$$n_{H_2} = n_{I_2} = \left(\frac{\alpha}{2}\right) 2 \text{ moles}; n_{HI} = (1 - \alpha)2 \text{ moles}$$

$$\text{Total moles} = n_{HI} + n_{H_2} + n_{I_2} = (1 - \alpha)2 + \alpha + \alpha = 2 \text{ moles}$$

The mole fractions of the species are then defined as

$$X_{HI} = \frac{n_{HI}}{\text{total moles}} = \frac{(1 - \alpha)2}{2} = (1 - \alpha) \qquad \text{3-15a}$$

$$X_{H_2} = \frac{n_{H_2}}{\text{total moles}} = \frac{\alpha}{2} \qquad \text{3-15b}$$

$$X_{I_2} = \frac{n_{I_2}}{\text{total moles}} = \frac{\alpha}{2} \qquad \text{3-15c}$$

The pressures of the species are given by the products of their mole fractions and the total pressure.

$$p_{I_2} = X_{I_2}P_t = \frac{\alpha}{2}P_t; p_{H_2} = X_{H_2}P_t = \frac{\alpha}{2}P_t; P_{HI} = X_{HI}P_t = (1 - \alpha)P_t \quad \textbf{3-15d}$$

On substitution from 3-15d in Eq. 3-14, we obtain

$$G_t = (1 - \alpha)2[\mu^0{}_{HI} + RT \ln(1 - \alpha)P_t] + \alpha\left[\mu^0{}_{H_2} + RT \ln \frac{\alpha P_t}{2}\right]$$

$$+ \alpha\left[\mu^0{}_{I_2} + RT \ln \frac{P_t}{2}\right] \qquad \textbf{3-16a}$$

and when $P_t = 2$ atm

$$G_t = (1 - \alpha)2[\mu^0{}_{HI} + RT \ln(1 - \alpha)2] + \alpha[\mu^0{}_{H_2} + RT \ln \alpha]$$

$$+ \alpha[\mu^0{}_{I_2} + RT \ln \alpha] \qquad \textbf{3-16b}$$

Let us calculate G_t for various values of α.

1 G_t when $\alpha = 0$

When α is zero, no hydrogen iodide has dissociated. Substituting for α in Eq. 3-16, the resulting equation is*

$$G_t = 2\mu^0{}_{HI} + 2RT \ln 2$$

As will be shown later, the numerical value of $\mu^0{}_{HI}$ equals $-2,713$ cal/mole; R is a constant with the numerical value 1.987 cal/(mole-°K), and T is the Kelvin temperature. For the system described above

$$G_t = 2(-2,713) + 2 \times 1.987 \times 666.8 \times 2.303 \log 2$$

$$G_t = -3,589 \text{ cal}$$

2 G_t when $\alpha = 1$

When α is unity, all the hydrogen iodide present has dissociated. When this value is substituted for α in Eq. 3-16

$$G_t = [\mu^0{}_{H_2} + RT \ln 1] + [\mu^0{}_{I_2} + RT \ln 1]$$

The numerical values of $\mu^0{}_{H_2}$ and $\mu^0{}_{I_2}$ are both zero and hence

$$G_t = 2RT \ln 1 = 0 \text{ cal}$$

3 G_t when $\alpha = 0.1$

At this point 10% of the hydrogen iodide present has dissociated, and on substituting for α in Eq. 3-16, the equation for G_t which results is

$$G_t = 1.8[\mu^0{}_{HI} + RT \ln 1.8] + 0.1[\mu^0{}_{H_2} + RT \ln 0.1] + 0.1[\mu^0{}_{I_2} + RT \ln 0.1]$$

---

* It should be noted that the limit of $\alpha \ln \alpha$ is zero as $\alpha \to 0$.

Putting in numerical values for the standard chemical potentials, and solving, we find

$$G_t = -4,091 \text{ cal}$$

Values of G_t for other values of α may be calculated in a similar fashion. The results of such mathematical operations are plotted in Figure 3-1, where it is seen that G_t at first decreases as α increases,

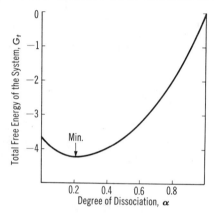

Figure 3-1   Variation of total free energy of a system as a function of the degree of dissociation. Initially 2 moles of $HI(g)$ at a pressure of 2 atmospheres at 666.8°K are placed in a flask of fixed volume. As the reaction, $2 HI(g) \rightleftharpoons H_2(g) + I_2(g)$, occurs, G_t varies with the composition of the reaction mixture. G_t is a minimum at $\alpha = 0.205$, which is the degree of dissociation at equilibrium.

goes through a minimum at $\alpha = 0.205$, and increases until G_t is 0 at $\alpha = 1$. The minimum in the plot corresponds to the minimum free energy attainable by this system. A chemical system at constant temperature and pressure tends to undergo chemical reaction until a minimum chemical potential energy is reached. When this state is achieved, the system is said to be at equilibrium, and further net reaction does not occur spontaneously. Thus, whenever the value of G_t for this system is greater than the minimum value, hydrogen and iodine will react to form hydrogen iodide, or hydrogen iodide will dissociate to form hydrogen and iodine, until the state of minimum free energy is achieved.

It is of interest to determine the relationship between α at the minimum value of G_t and the standard chemical potentials of the substances present in the system. At the minimum of the plot in Figure 3-1, the change of G_t with an infinitesimal change in α is zero, or in the language of the calculus, $dG_t/d\alpha = 0$. On differentiation of Eq.

32

3-16a, with respect to α, the result obtained is

$$\frac{dG_t}{d\alpha} = -2\mu^0{}_{HI} + \mu^0{}_{H_2} + \mu^0{}_{I_2} + RT \ln\left(\frac{\alpha^2 P_t{}^2}{4(1-\alpha)^2 P_t{}^2}\right) \qquad \textbf{3-17}$$

Setting $\dfrac{dG_t}{d\alpha} = 0$, and transposing

$$\mu^0{}_{H_2} + \mu^0{}_{I_2} - 2\mu^0{}_{HI} = -RT \ln\left(\frac{\alpha^2 P_t{}^2}{4(1-\alpha)^2 P_t{}^2}\right) \qquad \textbf{3-18}$$

The left-hand side of the equation is identical to ΔG^0 and is a constant for a particular temperature. At the minimum $\alpha = \alpha_{eq}$, and on substitution in Eq. 3-18

$$\Delta G^0 = -RT \ln\left(\frac{\alpha_{eq}{}^2 P_t{}^2}{4(1-\alpha_{eq})^2 P_t{}^2}\right) \qquad \textbf{3-19}$$

Because all the terms except the logarithmic terms are known to be constant, the logarithmic term itself must be constant. As we shall see shortly, this latter term is equal to the equilibrium constant for the dissociation of hydrogen iodide. Remembering that $p_i{}^0$ has been set as 1 atm, $a_i = p_i$ and we can write the equilibrium constant expression as

$$K^0{}_{diss} = \frac{(a_{H_2})_{eq}(a_{I_2})_{eq}}{(a_{HI})_{eq}{}^2} = \frac{(p_{H_2})_{eq}(p_{I_2})_{eq}}{(p_{HI})_{eq}{}^2} \qquad \textbf{3-20}$$

From Eqs. 3-15a–d the equilibrium pressures may be expressed in terms of α_{eq} and P_t as

$$(p_{H_2})_{eq} = (p_{I_2})_{eq} = \frac{\alpha_{eq}}{2} P_t$$

$$(p_{HI})_{eq} = (1 - \alpha_{eq})P_t$$

On substituting in the equilibrium constant expression, the equation for $K^0{}_{diss}$ is

$$K^0{}_{diss} = \frac{\alpha_{eq}{}^2 P_t{}^2}{4(1-\alpha_{eq})^2 P_t{}^2} \qquad \textbf{3-21}$$

The right-hand term is identical with the logarithmic term of Eq. 3-18. Therefore

$$\Delta G^0 = -RT \ln K^0{}_{diss} \qquad \textbf{3-22}$$

At the minimum value of G_t in Figure 3-1, the composition of the gaseous mixture is that of the equilibrium mixture. Taylor and Crist found that when 9.832×10^{-3} mole of hydrogen iodide was introduced into a one liter flask at $666.8°K$, only 7.816×10^{-3} mole of hydrogen iodide remained when equilibrium was established. From this information, an experimental value of α_{eq} can be calculated.

$$\alpha_{eq} = (9.832 - 7.816) \times 10^{-3}/9.832 \times 10^{-3} = 0.205$$

This value of α_{eq} corresponds exactly with that of the minimum in Figure 3-1. Once α_{eq} has been determined for hydrogen iodide dissociation, the equilibrium constant may be calculated by substituting in Eq. 3-20

$$K^0{}_{diss} = \frac{(0.205)(0.205)}{(1.590)^2} = 0.0166$$

ΔG^0 for the dissociation reaction (Eq. 3-12) is given by the equation

$$\Delta G^0 = -1.987 \times 666.8 \times 2.303 \times \log K^0{}_{diss} = +5.43 \text{ kcal}$$

For formation of hydrogen iodide by the reverse of the reaction shown by Eq. 3-12, $K_p{}^0 = 1/K^0{}_{diss} = 1/0.0166 = 60.2$, and $\Delta G^0 = -5.43$ kcal.

For students who are not familiar with calculus, the following derivation of the relationship between ΔG^0 and the equilibrium constant for a reaction may be somewhat more satisfying. It has already been stated that the change in free energy when a chemical reaction occurs equals the sum of the chemical potentials of the products *minus* the sum of the chemical potentials of the reactants. For the reaction represented by the equation

$$H_2(g, 1 \text{ atm}) + I_2(g, 1 \text{ atm}) \rightarrow 2 \text{ HI}(g, 1 \text{ atm}) \qquad \textbf{3-23}$$

the *gaseous species are in their standard states,* and hence

$$\Delta G = 2\,\mu^0{}_{HI} - \mu^0{}_{H_2} - \mu^0{}_{I_2} \equiv \Delta G^0 \qquad \textbf{3-24}$$

Note that this change in free energy corresponds to that of a rather unusual gaseous reaction, namely that in which the reactants in their standard states (1 atm pressure) are converted to products in their standard states (1 atm pressure). When the formation of hydrogen iodide occurs at conditions different from standard state conditions, $\Delta G \neq \Delta G^0$; ΔG corresponds to the change in free energy when one mole of iodine at pressure p_{I_2} reacts with one mole of hydrogen at pressure p_{H_2} to form two moles of hydrogen iodide at pressure p_{HI}. In general, ΔG is given by the equation

$$\Delta G = 2\mu_{HI} - \mu_{H_2} - \mu_{I_2} \qquad \textbf{3-25}$$

From Eq. 3-6 and the fact that all $p_i{}^0$ values are 1 atm

$$\Delta G = 2\mu^0{}_{HI} + 2RT \ln p_{HI} - \mu^0{}_{I_2} - RT \ln p_{I_2} - \mu^0{}_{H_2} - RT \ln p_{H_2} \qquad \textbf{3-26}$$

Collecting terms and substituting for ΔG^0 from Eq. 3-24

$$\Delta G = \Delta G^0 + RT \ln \frac{(p_{HI})^2}{(p_{I_2})(p_{H_2})} \qquad \textbf{3-27}$$

The logarithmic term on the right is defined as Q^0. It has the same form as the equilibrium constant but the activities or pressures are those existing in the reaction mixture. On substitution

$$\Delta G = \Delta G^0 + RT \ln Q^0 \qquad \textbf{3-28}$$

For a system at chemical equilibrium, there is no force causing a net reaction and the sum of the chemical potentials of the reactants is equal to that of the products. For the hydrogen iodide system at chemical equilibrium

$$2\mu_{HI} = \mu_{I_2} + \mu_{H_2} \qquad \textbf{3-29}$$

On.combination with Eq. 3-25 we see that $\Delta G = 0$. When this condition exists, the pressures of all gases present are the equilibrium pressures, and $Q^0 = K_p{}^0$. Hence on substitution of these conditions in Eq. 3-28, we obtain

$$\Delta G^0 = -RT \ln K_p{}^0 \qquad \textbf{3-30}$$

ΔG^0 is the free energy change for the formation of two moles of hydrogen iodide in its standard state from the elements in their standard states. ΔG^0 was shown to be -5.43 kcal. For the formation of one mole of hydrogen iodide under these conditions, the free energy change is $\Delta G^0/2$ and is known as the *free energy of formation*, ΔG^0_f. It has the numerical value $-5.43/2 = -2.72$ kcal/mole.

It can be shown that μ^0_{HI} is equal to ΔG^0_f for hydrogen iodide. The values of μ^0_i for hydrogen and iodine at $666.8°K$ in their most stable states at one atmosphere pressure are zero. On substitution of these values in Eq. 3-24, the result is

$$\Delta G^0 = 2\mu^0_{HI} \qquad \textbf{3-31}$$

Therefore

$$\mu^0_{HI} = \Delta G^0/2 = \Delta G^0_f = -2.72 \text{ kcal}$$

For any chemical substance, ΔG^0_f may be taken as equal to μ^0_i at that temperature.

It should be realized that Eq. 3-30 is a generally applicable equation which provides a means of obtaining ΔG^0_f or μ^0_i for a compound. One has only to obtain $K_p{}^0$ and ΔG^0 for the formation of the compound from the elements, and then calculate the free energy of formation per mole of the compound.

For the formation of ammonia as shown by the equation

$$N_2(g) + 3 H_2(g) \rightleftharpoons 2 NH_3(g) \qquad \text{3-32}$$

the equilibrium constant K_p was found to be 0.119 at 500°K. Therefore

$$\Delta G^0 = -2.303 \times 1.987 \times 500 \times \log(0.119) = +2{,}120 \text{ cal}$$

Hence

$$\Delta G^0{}_f = \mu^0{}_{NH_3} = 2{,}120/2 = +1{,}060 \text{ cal at 500°K.}$$

The standard free energy change for the dissociation reaction

$$N_2F_4(g) \rightleftharpoons 2 NF_2(g) \qquad \text{3-33}$$

can also be calculated from Eq. 3-30. $K_p{}^0$ is 2.91×10^{-2} at 423°K. Therefore

$$\Delta G^0 = -2.303 \times 1.987 \times 423 \times \log(2.91 \times 10^{-2}) = +2{,}970 \text{ cal}$$

The standard free energy change for any reaction may be calculated if the values of the standard free energies of formation of the reactants and products are known. Table 3-1 contains such values for a limited number of substances. The standard free energy change for a reaction is the sum of the free energies of formation of the products minus the sum of the free energies of formation of the reactants. Since $\mu^0{}_i = \Delta G^0{}_f$, the standard free energy change for the reaction represented by Eq. 3-4 is given by either Eq. 3-10 or by 3-34

$$\Delta G^0 = (c\,\Delta G^0{}_{f(C)} + d\,\Delta G^0{}_{f(D)} + e\,\Delta G^0{}_{f(E)}) - (a\,\Delta G^0{}_{f(A)}$$
$$+ b\,\Delta G^0{}_{f(B)}) \qquad \text{3-34}$$

For example, it is possible to calculate the standard free energy change for the chemical reaction between carbon dioxide and hydrogen at 298°K from the data in Table 3-1 and the fact that the free energy of formation of hydrogen gas in its standard state at that temperature is zero. The equation for the reaction is

$$CO_2(g, 1 \text{ atm}) + H_2(g, 1 \text{ atm}) \rightarrow CO(g, 1 \text{ atm}) + H_2O(g, 1 \text{ atm}) \qquad \text{3-35}$$

The standard free energy change is given by

$$\Delta G^0 = \mu^0{}_{CO_2} + \mu^0{}_{H_2O} - \mu^0{}_{CO_2} - \mu^0{}_{H_2} \qquad \text{3-36}$$

or

$$\Delta G^0 = \Delta G^0{}_{f(CO)} + \Delta G^0{}_{f(H_2O)} - \Delta G^0{}_{f(CO_2)} - \Delta G^0{}_{f(H_2)} \qquad \text{3-37}$$
$$\Delta G^0 = (-32.808) + (-54.635) - (-94.260) - 0$$
$$\Delta G^0 = +6.817 \text{ kcal}$$

Similarly, for the formation of nitrosyl chloride as shown by the equation

Table III-1

Standard Free Energies and Standard Enthalpies of Formation and Entropies at 298°K.

Formula	ΔG^0_f (kcal)	ΔH^0_f (kcal)	S^0 (entropy units)	Formula	ΔG^0_f (kcal)	ΔH^0_f (kcal)	S^0 (entropy units)
$HF(g)$	−64.7	−64.2	41.97	$H_2(g)$	0	0	31.21
$HCl(g)$	−22.769	−22.063	44.62	$F_2(g)$	0	0	48.6
$HBr(g)$	−12.72	−8.66	47.44	$Cl_2(g)$	0	0	53.29
$HI(g)$	0.31	6.2	49.31	$Br_2(g)$	0.751	7.34	58.64
$HI(l)$	0	0	—	$Br_2(l)$	0	0	36.4
$H_2O(g)$	−54.635	−57.798	45.11	$I_2(g)$	4.63	14.88	62.28
$H_2O(l)$	−56.690	−68.317	16.72	$I_2(s)$	0	0	27.9
$H_2O_2(l)$	−27.240	−44.84	22	$O_2(g)$	0	0	49.00
$H_2S(g)$	−7.892	−4.815	49.15	$O_3(g)$	39.06	34.0	56.8
$SO_2(g)$	−71.79	−70.76	59.40	$BrCl(g)$	−0.210	3.51	57.34
$SO_3(g)$	−88.52	−94.45	61.24	$ICl(g)$	−1.32	4.2	59.12
$NH_3(g)$	−3.976	−11.04	46.01	$IBr(g)$	0.91	9.75	61.8
$NO(g)$	20.719	21.600	50.339	$AgF(s)$	−44.2	−48.5	20
$NO_2(g)$	12.390	8.091	57.47	$AgCl(s)$	−26.224	−30.362	22.97
$N_2O_4(g)$	23.491	2.309	72.73	$AgBr(s)$	−22.930	−23.78	25.60
$NOCl(g)$	15.86	12.57	63.0	$AgI(s)$	−15.85	−14.91	27.3
$CO(g)$	−32.808	−26.416	47.30	$AgNO_2(s)$	4.744	−10.605	30.62
$CO_2(g)$	−94.260	−94.052	51.061	$AgSCN(s)$	23.3	21.0	—
C (graphite)	0	0	1.3609	$TlBr(s)$	−39.7	−41.2	28.6
C (diamond)	0.4532	0.6850	0.5829	$TlCl(s)$	−44.19	−48.99	25.9
$Na(s)$	0	0	12.2	$NaF(s)$	−129.3	−136.0	14.0
$K(s)$	0	0	15.2	$NaCl(s)$	−91.785	−98.232	17.30
$Ag(s)$	0	0	10.206	$NaI(s)$	−56.7	−68.64	22.1
$Tl(s)$	0	0	15.4	$KCl(s)$	−97.592	−104.175	19.76
$N_2(g)$	0	0	45.767	$BaSO_4(s)$	−323.4	−350.2	31.6

Data from W. M. Latimer, *Oxidation Potentials* (1952), Prentice-Hall, New York.

37

$$2 \text{ NO}(g, 1 \text{ atm}) + \text{Cl}_2(g, 1 \text{ atm}) \rightarrow 2 \text{ NOCl}(g, 1 \text{ atm}) \qquad \textbf{3-38}$$
$$\Delta G^0 = 2\Delta G^0{}_{f(\text{NOCl})} - 2\Delta G^0{}_{f(\text{NO})} - \Delta G^0{}_{f(\text{Cl}_2)} \qquad \textbf{3-39}$$
$$\Delta G^0 = 2(15.86) - 2(20.72) - 0$$
$$\Delta G^0 = -9.72 \text{ kcal}$$

Observe that in Table 3-1 there are two values for the standard free energy of formation of water. At one atmosphere pressure at 298°K, the free energy of formation of gaseous water is -54.635 kcal. This represents the free energy change for the reaction shown by the equation

$$\text{H}_2(g, 1 \text{ atm}) + 1/2 \text{ O}_2(g, 1 \text{ atm}) \rightarrow \text{H}_2\text{O}(g, 1 \text{ atm}) \qquad \textbf{3-40}$$

At 298°K, water is a liquid in its most stable state at one atmosphere. If the reaction is that shown by the equation

$$\text{H}_2(g, 1 \text{ atm}) + 1/2 \text{ O}_2(g, 1 \text{ atm}) \rightarrow \text{H}_2\text{O}(l, 1 \text{ atm}) \qquad \textbf{3-41}$$

then the free energy change is -56.690 kcal. Thus, for the formation of liquid water from the elements, the free energy change is more negative than that for the formation of gaseous water. For the conversion of gaseous water to liquid water as shown by the equation

$$\text{H}_2\text{O}(g, 1 \text{ atm}) \rightarrow \text{H}_2\text{O}(l, 1 \text{ atm}) \qquad \textbf{3-42}$$

the free energy change is given by

$$\Delta G^0 = \Delta G^0{}_{f(\text{liquid})} - \Delta G^0{}_{f(\text{gas})} \qquad \textbf{3-43}$$
$$\Delta G^0 = -56.690 - (-54.635)$$
$$\Delta G^0 = -2.055 \text{ kcal}$$

As all students know, gaseous water at one atmosphere pressure at 298°K spontaneously condenses to the liquid. This is in accord with a negative value of ΔG^0 for the process.

Note also that the free energies of formation (or the standard chemical potentials) of certain elemental substances listed in Table 3-1 are not zero. This is because these substances as listed are not in their most stable states at one atmosphere pressure at 298°K. Bromine is a liquid and iodine is a solid when they are in their most stable forms. Hence the free energies of formation of the gases are positive. For oxygen, the most stable molecular form of the element that can exist at 298°K and one atmosphere pressure is O_2, not O_3. Hence the free energy of formation of O_3 from O_2 is positive.

It has been stated for any chemical reaction, that Eq. 3-24 gives the value of the change in free energy when the reactants in their standard states react to produce the products in their standard states. *For any other set of conditions*, the change in free energy is given by

$$\Delta G = -RT \ln K_p^0 + RT \ln Q^0 \qquad \textbf{3-44}$$

or

$$\Delta G = -RT \ln K_p^0 / Q^0 \qquad \textbf{3-45}$$

These equations result from combining Eqs. 3-28 and 3-30. A spontaneous process at constant temperature and pressure requires that ΔG be negative and that K_p^0 be greater than Q^0. The same relation between K_p^0 and Q^0 was obtained earlier from a consideration of chemical kinetics. For a mixture of nitrogen and hydrogen at elevated temperatures, Q^0 is initially equal to zero if no ammonia is present, and ΔG must be $-\infty$. As the reaction proceeds, Q^0 increases and approaches K_p^0 with the consequence that ΔG becomes less negative. When Q^0 equals K_p^0, ΔG equals 0, and equilibrium is established; no further net chemical reaction will occur.

3–D   FREE ENERGY CHANGES AND ENTHALPY CHANGES

Because early workers incorrectly identified spontaneity of chemical reactions with enthalpy changes, the question which arises is "What relationship, if any, does exist between the enthalpy change and the free energy change for a chemical reaction?" Again we should refer to material discussed in Chapter 2 and, because of the relationship just established between ΔG^0 and K_p^0, determine what relationship exists between ΔH^0 and K_p^0. ΔH^0 is the enthalpy change which occurs when reactants in their standard states react to produce products in their standard states. To begin, the Arrhenius equation

$$k = A\, e^{-E^{\ddagger}/RT} \qquad \textbf{3-46}$$

provides the relationship between the absolute temperature, the activation energy $E^{\ddagger}$, and the specific reaction rate constant for a chemical reaction. It can be shown that the Arrhenius activation energy is related to the enthalpy of activation, $H^{\ddagger}$, by the equation

$$H^{\ddagger} = E^{\ddagger} - RT + \Delta n^{\ddagger} RT \qquad \textbf{3-47}$$

where $\Delta n^{\ddagger}$ is the number of molecules of the activated complex (always 1) minus the number of molecules reacting to form the activated complex. For liquid and solid reactants, for monomolecular dissociation of gases, and for reactions at low temperature, $E^{\ddagger}$ is approximately equal to $H^{\ddagger}$. As an approximation, we will rewrite the Arrhenius equation as

$$k = A\, e^{-H^{\ddagger}/RT} \qquad \textbf{3-48}$$

The standard enthalpy change for the chemical reaction is equal to the difference in activation enthalpies of the forward and reverse reactions

$$\Delta H = H_f{}^{\ddagger} - H_r{}^{\ddagger} \cong \Delta H^0 \qquad \textbf{3-49}$$

How is ΔH^0 related to the rate constants and to the temperature? Consider the formation of hydrogen iodide from hydrogen and iodine gases.

$$H_2(g) + I_2(g) \underset{k_r}{\overset{k_f}{\rightleftharpoons}} 2\,HI(g) \qquad \textbf{3-50}$$

For the forward reaction, the rate constant is

$$k_f = A_f\,e^{-H_f{}^{\ddagger}/RT} \qquad \textbf{3-51}$$

and for the reverse reaction, the decomposition of hydrogen iodide, the rate constant is

$$k_r = A_r\,e^{-H_r{}^{\ddagger}/RT} \qquad \textbf{3-52}$$

The equilibrium constant $K_p{}^0$ for Eq. 3-50 is equal to the ratio of the forward and reverse rate constants. Making the proper substitutions

$$K_p{}^0 = k_f/k_r = \frac{A_f\,e^{-H_f{}^{\ddagger}/RT}}{A_r\,e^{-H_r{}^{\ddagger}/RT}} \qquad \textbf{3-53}$$

Taking the natural logarithms and simplifying

$$\ln K_p{}^0 = -H_f{}^{\ddagger}/RT + H_r{}^{\ddagger}/RT + \ln A_f/A_r \qquad \textbf{3-54}$$

Substituting from Eq. 3-49

$$\ln K_p{}^0 = -\Delta H^0/RT + \ln A_f/A_r \qquad \textbf{3-55}$$

Substituting ΔG^0 from Eq. 3-30, we obtain

$$\Delta G^0 = \Delta H^0 - T(R \ln A_f/A_r) \qquad \textbf{3-56}$$

This equation states in effect that the free energy change equals the enthalpy change minus a term dependent on the absolute temperature and the gas constant multiplied by the logarithm of the ratio of two constants. This is, for the moment, the desired relationship between ΔG^0 and ΔH^0, and while derived for the case of the reaction of hydrogen and iodine, it is actually of general application.

Let us explore further the implications of Eq. 3-55. On differentiation of this equation with respect to the absolute temperature, we obtain the equation

$$\frac{d \ln K_p{}^0}{dT} = \frac{\Delta H^0}{RT^2} \qquad \textbf{3-57}$$

which was first obtained by Van't Hoff prior to the advent of the Arrhenius equation. Eq. 3-57 can also be written in the integrated form

$$\log \frac{K_2{}^0}{K_1{}^0} = \frac{-\Delta H^0}{2.303R}\left[\frac{1}{T_2} - \frac{1}{T_1}\right] \qquad \textbf{3-58}$$

where $K_2{}^0$ and $K_1{}^0$ are the equilibrium constants at temperatures T_2 and T_1, respectively. Thus if $K_p{}^0$ is known at any two temperatures, ΔH^0 can be calculated.

For the formation of hydrogen iodide, $K_p{}^0$ is 60.2 at 666.8°K and 49.6 at 731°K. On substitution into Eq. 3-58

$$\log \frac{60.2}{49.6} = \frac{-\Delta H^0}{2.303 \times 1.987}\left[\frac{1}{667} - \frac{1}{731}\right]$$

$$\Delta H^0 = -2.89 \times 10^3 \text{ cal} \quad or \quad -3 \text{ kcal}$$

Similarly, for the dissociation reaction

$$N_2F_4(g) \rightleftharpoons 2\,NF_2(g) \qquad \textbf{3-59}$$

the equilibrium constant K_p is 1.21×10^{-3} at 373°K and 2.91×10^{-2} at 423°K. On substitution into Eq. 3-58

$$\log \frac{1.21 \times 10^{-3}}{2.91 \times 10^{-3}} = \frac{-\Delta H^0}{2.303R}\left[\frac{1}{373} - \frac{1}{423}\right]$$

$$\Delta H^0 = \frac{1.383 \times 2.303 \times 1.987}{0.00032} = 19,800 \text{ cal} \quad or \quad 19.8 \text{ kcal}$$

Equation 3-55 predicts that a plot of $\log K_p{}^0$ *vs.* $1/T$ should be a straight line with a slope equal to $-\Delta H^0/2.303R$. This is in fact a widely used method of estimating ΔH^0 and does yield a straight line provided ΔH^0 is constant over the temperature range investigated. A more precise value can be obtained by this method than by calculation using only data from two temperatures. Figure 3-2 is such a plot for the N_2F_4 dissociation reaction. The value obtained for the slope is

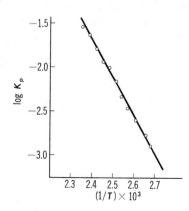

Figure 3-2 Plot of $\log K_p$ *vs.* $1/T$ for the dissociation of $N_2F_4(g)$. Slope = -4.24×10^3.

-4.24×10^3. Therefore

$$\frac{-\Delta H^0}{2.303R} = -4.24 \times 10^3$$

$\Delta H^0 = 2.303 \times 1.987 \times 4.24 \times 10^3 = 19{,}500$ cal   or   19.5 kcal

The enthalpy change of a reaction may also be obtained by direct measurement. For example, the heat liberated when carbon and oxygen combine to form carbon dioxide may be determined by placing a weighed amount of carbon in an excess of oxygen in a calorimeter and then causing them to react. A calorimeter is a device for determining the amount of heat produced or absorbed by a chemical reaction.

The standard enthalpy change, ΔH^0, for any reaction is equal to the sum of the standard enthalpies of formation $(\Delta H^0{}_f)$ of the products minus the sum of the standard enthalpies of formation of the reactants. For a reaction such as that in Eq. 3-4, ΔH^0 is given by the equation

$$\Delta H^0 = (c\,\Delta H^0{}_{f(C)} + d\,\Delta H^0{}_{f(D)} + e\,\Delta H^0{}_{f(E)}) - (a\,\Delta H^0{}_{f(A)} + b\,\Delta H^0{}_{f(B)})$$

3-60

This is a mathematical statement of Hess' law which is important in calculating standard enthalpies of reactions, provided that values of $\Delta H^0{}_f$ for the various species are known. For any *element* in its most stable form at one atmosphere pressure at any temperature, $\Delta H^0{}_f$ is taken as zero.

For the reaction of carbon dioxide at 25°C and one atmosphere pressure as shown by the equation

$$C(s,\text{ graphite}) + O_2(g,\text{ 1 atm}) \rightarrow CO_2(g,\text{ 1 atm}) \qquad \textbf{3-61}$$

the enthalpy change ΔH^0 for the reaction was found experimentally to be -94.05 kcal/mole; ΔH^0 also equals the standard enthalpy of formation of carbon dioxide as the following equations show:

$$\Delta H^0 = \Delta H^0{}_{f(CO_2)} - \Delta H^0{}_{f(O_2)} - \Delta H^0{}_{f(C)} \qquad \textbf{3-62}$$

$$-94.05 = \Delta H^0{}_{f(CO_2)} - 0 - 0$$

$$\Delta H^0{}_{f(CO)_2} = -94.05 \text{ kcal/mole}$$

Similarly, for the formation of nitrosyl chloride at 25°C, as shown by Eq. 3-63

$$2\,NO(g,\text{ 1 atm}) + Cl_2(g,\text{ 1 atm}) \rightarrow 2\,NOCl(g,\text{ 1 atm}) \qquad \textbf{3-63}$$

$$\Delta H^0 = 2\Delta H^0{}_{f(NOCl)} - 2\Delta H^0{}_{f(NO)} - \Delta H^0{}_{f(Cl_2)}$$

$$\Delta H^0 = 2(12.57) - 2(21.60) - 0$$

$$\Delta H^0 = -18.06 \text{ kcal}$$

3–E   FREE ENERGY CHANGES AND ENTROPY CHANGES

Some chemical reactions having a positive value of ΔH do occur spontaneously because ΔG is less than zero. Absorption of heat is usually associated with the achievement of a higher energy state. The question is therefore raised as to what properties of a system offset the absorption of heat sufficiently so that a reaction can occur. The answer is that systems spontaneously tend to achieve the most random orientation possible, or the most disordered state. In some instances these tendencies are great enough to offset the endothermic characters of reactions. Other reactions which are exothermic may not occur if great decreases in the randomness of the systems result.

The disorder of a system is described in terms of a quantity known as *entropy*. The entropy S is a thermodynamic function of the state of the system and is a measure of the number of ways N by which a particular state of the system may be arranged. Entropy may be defined as $S = R \ln N$. For example, crystalline neon at $0°K$ has only one way in which the atoms may fit into the crystal lattice to form a perfect crystal, and hence its entropy is zero. When the temperature is raised sufficiently so that neon is a gas, the atoms are free to move around and a large number of arrangements of the atoms is possible. Hence the entropy of the gas at any temperature is higher than the entropy of the solid at $0°K$. In general, solids are more ordered than liquids which in turn are more ordered than gases. Hence the entropy of a particular substance increases as it is converted from a solid to a liquid to a gas as the temperature of the substance is increased.

The change in entropy ΔS in going from State 1 to State 2 is a function only of the state of the system and is independent of the path by which the change occurs. $\Delta S = S_2 - S_1$. If there are N_2 ways of achieving State 2 and N_1 ways of achieving State 1

$$\Delta S = R \ln \frac{N_2}{N_1} \qquad \textbf{3-64}$$

Consider for a moment some simple process for which ΔH^0 is zero, such as the mixing of two gases behaving ideally. Assume that equal volumes of helium and neon at the same temperature and 1 atm pressure are enclosed in containers separated by a stopcock as shown in Figure 3-3.

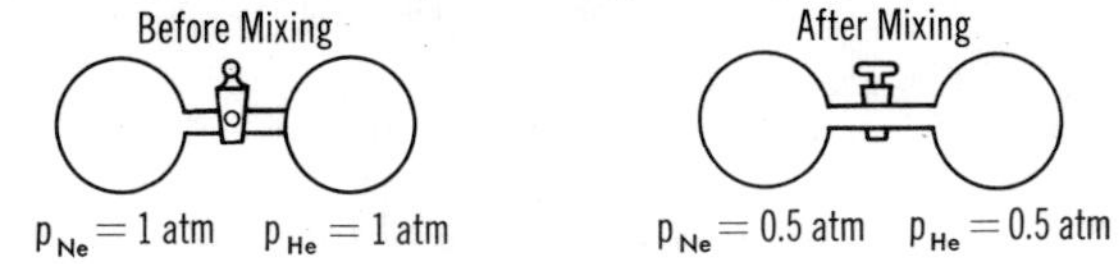

Before Mixing   After Mixing

$p_{Ne} = 1\,atm$ $p_{He} = 1\,atm$ $p_{Ne} = 0.5\,atm$ $p_{He} = 0.5\,atm$

Figure 3-3 Vessel containing two gases before and after mixing.

43

If the stopcock between the two sides of the vessel is opened, the gases will mix and eventually the gases in the two flasks will have the same composition. One-half of the molecules in each flask will be helium and the other half will be neon. Since there is no chemical reaction between these gases, ΔH and ΔE are both zero. What is the driving force which causes this mixing? Again, it is a natural tendency for systems to go from an ordered state to one of disorder. In the case under discussion, the situation with each gas in a separate container is more highly ordered than that with each gas spread throughout both containers. Every gas molecule has the choice of being in either of the two containers after mixing, whereas it was restricted to one of them before mixing. There is therefore an increase in entropy on mixing the two gases.

It is now necessary to relate the term $(R \ln A_f/A_r)$ from Eq. 3-56 to the entropy changes for a chemical reaction. It should be recalled that the constants A_f and A_r came originally from the Arrhenius equation and are related to the probability of a collision occurring with an orientation suitable for reaction. While it is not obvious, $R \ln A_f/A_r = \Delta S^0$, where ΔS^0 for a chemical reaction is the sum of the entropies of the products minus the sum of the entropies of the reactants. ΔS^0 is positive for a chemical reaction which is accompanied by an increase in randomness of the system. On substitution into Eq. 3-56, the free energy change of a chemical reaction at constant temperature then becomes

$$\Delta G^0 = \Delta H^0 - T \Delta S^0 \qquad \textbf{3-65}$$

when both reactants and products are in their standard states. At other activities of reactants and products

$$\Delta G = \Delta H - T \Delta S \qquad \textbf{3-66}$$

These equations can also be derived by the considerations of chemical thermodynamics and are a consequence of the Second Law of Thermodynamics.

Since ΔH^0 and ΔG^0 for the N_2F_4 dissociation have been determined, it is now possible to determine ΔS^0. At $423°K$, ΔG^0 was 2,970 cal and ΔH^0 was 19,500 cal. Substituting in the above equation

$$2,970 = 19,500 - 423 \Delta S^0$$

$$\Delta S^0 = \frac{-2,970 + 19,500}{423} = 39 \text{ cal/(mole-°K) or 39 entropy units (e.u.)}$$

ΔS^0 is positive for this reaction and this tends to offset, in part, the very positive heat of reaction. ΔH^0 and ΔS^0 are essentially independent of temperature, but the $T\Delta S^0$ term will become larger as T increases because ΔS^0 is positive. Because $T\Delta S^0$ is subtracted from ΔH^0, ΔG^0 becomes more negative as T increases and hence the dissociation reaction should occur to a greater extent with increasing temperature. This was shown earlier to be the case for the N_2F_4 reaction by the plot in Figure 2-8.

The foregoing represents a method of determining ΔS^0 for a chemical reaction once ΔG^0 and ΔH^0 have been determined. It is also possible to calculate ΔS^0 for any chemical reaction if the absolute entropies of the reacting species and products are known. By thermochemical measurements, it is possible to obtain absolute values of the entropies of elements and compounds at various temperatures. In Table 3-1, values of entropies for a few substances at 298°K are listed. For any chemical reaction, such as shown in Eq. 3-4, the change in entropy is equal to the sum of the entropies of the products minus the sum of the entropies of the reactants

$$\Delta S^0 = (c\,S^0{}_\text{C} + d\,S^0{}_\text{D} + e\,S^0{}_\text{E}) - (a\,S^0{}_\text{A} + b\,S^0{}_\text{B}) \qquad \textbf{3-67}$$

For the formation of nitrosyl chloride as illustrated in Eq. 3-63, ΔS^0 at 298°K is given by the equation

$$\Delta S^0 = 2S^0{}_\text{NOCl} - 2S^0{}_\text{NO} - S^0{}_{\text{Cl}_2} \qquad \textbf{3-68}$$

The values of the entropies of these species may be obtained from Table 3-1. On substitution, we obtain

$$\Delta S^0 = 2(63.0) - 2(50.4) - 53.3$$
$$\Delta S^0 = -28.1 \text{ cal/(mole-°K)}$$

Since we have previously calculated values for ΔG^0 and ΔH^0 for this reaction, we can also estimate ΔS^0 from Eq. 3-65. On rearranging, and substituting, we obtain the same value for ΔS^0

$$\Delta S^0 = \frac{\Delta H^0 - \Delta G^0}{T} = \frac{-18,060 + 9,720}{298} = -28.1 \text{ cal/(mole-°K)}$$

On a molecular basis, what is the explanation for an increase or decrease in entropy? Whenever a reaction occurs where there are more product molecules (or individual atoms) than reactant molecules, the system goes to a state of greater disorder. At sufficiently high temperatures, all molecules become unstable because of the positive entropy change associated with dissociation, and eventually they dissociate into atoms. When there are fewer product molecules than reactant molecules, the system is more ordered and there is a decrease in entropy.

What is the basis for a decrease in enthalpy? Generally a reaction has a decrease in enthalpy when the bonds formed between atoms of the product molecules are more stable than those of the reactant molecules. This means that the product molecules have a lower enthalpy state than the reactant molecules. Enthalpy changes are usually associated with the making and breaking of chemical bonds.

Most chemical reactions are carried out in closed systems at constant temperature and pressure. Under these conditions, a spontaneous chemical reaction must be accompanied by a decrease in Gibbs free energy. As shown by Eq. 3-66, there are two terms which together determine the value of the free energy change; these are the enthalpy change ΔH and the product of the absolute temperature and the entropy change $T\Delta S$. These two terms may enhance each other or they may oppose each other. As a result, there are four possible combinations of terms leading to the values of the free energy.

Sign of ΔH	Sign of ΔS	Sign of ΔG	Spontaneity at constant T and P
−	+	−	Spontaneous
−	−	+ or −	Depends on relative magnitude
+	+	+ or −	of the two terms
+	−	+	Not spontaneous

3–F SPONTANEITY UNDER CONDITIONS OTHER THAN CONSTANT T AND P

Occasionally, reactions are carried out in closed systems at constant temperature and volume. Under these conditions, a different free energy, the Helmholtz free energy, ΔA, must be negative for a spontaneous process

$$\Delta A = \Delta E - T\Delta S \qquad \text{3-69}$$

In this equation ΔE is the energy change when the reaction occurs at constant volume. The criterion that ΔA be negative for reactions occurring at constant temperature and volume is parallel to the criterion at constant temperature and pressure.

A different criterion of spontaneity is required for a system so isolated from its surroundings that the energy and the volume are constant. Under these conditions, the necessary requirement for a spontaneous change is that the disorder of the system increases. ΔS must be positive.

A special case that corresponds to conditions often encountered in the laboratory involves open systems under atmospheric pressure at constant temperature. For reactions where only liquids or solids with low vapor pressures are involved, the system can be treated essentially as one at constant pressure. When gaseous reactants or products are involved, the situation is considerably more complicated, and the escape of one of the reactants or products may cause the reaction to go to completion even though the thermodynamic properties for a closed system are unfavorable.

Consider a closed evacuated container in which solid NH_4HS is placed. The compound decomposes partially as shown by the equation

$$NH_4HS(s) \rightleftharpoons NH_3(g) + H_2S(g)$$

until equilibrium is established. At 298°K, the equilibrium pressures of $NH_3(g)$ and $H_2S(g)$ are each 250 mm of Hg. If the system remains closed, once these pressures are achieved, there is no further decrease in the amount of $NH_4HS(s)$. However, in a container open to the atmosphere, NH_3 and H_2S escape and their pressures over the $NH_4HS(s)$ are insufficient to maintain equilibrium even though the total pressure (air, NH_3, and H_2S) equals 760 mm of Hg. Consequently, there will be a net dissociation of $NH_4HS(s)$ and this process will continue until all of the solid NH_4HS has dissociated. In effect, by removal of one or more of the products, Q^0 is made less than K_p^0, and ΔG is less than zero. Hence, the reaction in an open container tends to occur spontaneously.

Problems

3-1 From the data presented in Table 3-1, determine ΔG^0, ΔH^0, ΔS^0, and K_p at 25°C for the reactions represented by the following equations:
  (a) $4\ NH_3(g) + 5\ O_2(g) \rightarrow 4\ NO(g) + 6\ H_2O(g)$
  (b) $4\ NH_3(g) + 5\ O_2(g) \rightarrow 4\ NO(g) + 6\ H_2O(l)$
  (c) $N_2O_4(g) \rightarrow 2\ NO_2(g)$
  (d) $SO_2(g) + NO_2(g) \rightarrow SO_3(g) + NO(g)$
  (e) $H_2S(g) + O_2(g) \rightarrow SO_2(g) + H_2O(g)$

3-2 From the following data for the reaction

$$2\ HI(g) \rightarrow H_2(g) + I_2(g)$$

make a plot of log K_p^0 *vs.* $1/T$.

Temperature	K_p^0
764°K	2.192×10^{-2}
731°K	2.018×10^{-2}
699°K	1.812×10^{-2}
667°K	1.64×10^{-2}

Determine ΔH^0, ΔS^0, and ΔG^0 at 750°K.

47

3-3   Determine $\Delta H^0, \Delta S^0$, and ΔG^0 at 1450°K for the following reaction at a total pressure of 1 atmosphere.

$$2\,CO_2(g) \rightleftharpoons 2\,CO(g) + O_2(g)$$

Temperature, °K	% Dissociation of CO_2
1395	0.0142
1400	0.015
1443	0.025
1478	0.032
1498	0.047
1565	0.064

3-4   At 1000°K, ΔG^0 for formation of NH_3 as shown by the equation

$$N_2(g) + 3\,H_2(g) \rightleftharpoons 2\,NH_3(g)$$

is $+29.53$ kcal. A mixture containing all three gases is prepared in which the pressure of each gas is one atmosphere. What reaction, if any, will occur spontaneously at this temperature?

3-5   The standard free energy change at 2000°K for the reaction represented by the equation

$$2\,NO(g) \rightleftharpoons N_2(g) + O_2(g)$$

is -32.0 kcal. If a mixture is prepared with 3 moles of NO, 2 moles of N_2, and 4 moles of O_2 in a 1 liter container at this temperature, what reaction, if any, will occur spontaneously? If a reaction occurs, what are the final pressures of each species present?

3-6 ΔG^0 is 730 cal at 1000°K for the reaction represented by the equation

$$CO_2(g) + H_2(g) \rightleftharpoons H_2O(g) + CO(g)$$

If a mixture of 1 mole of H_2 and 2 moles of CO_2 is placed in a 5 liter container, what fraction of the CO_2 has been consumed when equilibrium is established? What are the pressures of each of the species present?

3-7   At 500°K the values of the standard chemical potentials for $I_2(g)$ and $Br_2(g)$ are 0 and the value for $IBr(g)$ is -2.03 kcal/mole. For a system containing initially 2 moles of $IBr(g)$ at a pressure of 2 atmospheres, make a plot of G_t *vs.* the fraction of IBr dissociated as the reaction represented by the following equation occurs:

$$2\,IBr(g) \rightleftharpoons I_2(g) + Br_2(g)$$

From the plot, determine an approximate value of K_p^0. Calculate an exact value of K_p^0 from the data presented.

CHAPTER 4

Homogeneous Equilibria in Aqueous Solution

Many properties of acids and bases were known for centuries before these substances were thoroughly understood. Acidic substances were observed to change the color of the organic dye litmus from blue to red and to have a sharp or sour taste. Bases, or alkalies, were observed to be soapy or slippery to the touch and to change the color of litmus from red to blue. It was further known that acids and bases neutralized each other to form a class of compounds called *salts*. At one time, it was proposed that oxygen was a common constituent of all acids. Later, the belief was that hydrogen rather than oxygen was the element responsible for the acidic properties of substances. While this is generally true for aqueous systems, it is now realized that neither hydrogen nor oxygen is necessary for a substance to show acidic properties. Eventually, with the results of the investigations carried on over several centuries, rational concepts of acids and bases were developed.

4–A ACID-BASE CONCEPTS

1 The Arrhenius Concept

To account for the colligative properties and electrical conductivity of aqueous solutions of acids, bases, and salts, Arrhenius proposed that these substances were dissociated, to a greater or lesser extent, into positively and negatively charged ions. Arrhenius found that the differences in electrical conductivity of aqueous solutions could be explained on the basis that solutions which were highly conducting contained extensively dissociated solutes, while those solutions which were weakly conducting contained slightly dissociated solutes. The former were called *strong electrolytes* while the latter were known as *weak electrolytes.* Those solutes which did not alter the conductivity of the water were considered to be undissociated and were called *nonelectrolytes.*

According to Arrhenius' theory, acids were hydrogen-containing substances which produced hydrogen ions in aqueous solution by dissociation, and bases were hydroxide-containing substances which produced hydroxide ions in aqueous solution. In water, hydrogen chloride was a strong acid because it dissociated to a high degree into H^+ and Cl^- ions, while acetic acid was a weak acid because it dissociated only slightly into ions. Similarly, sodium hydroxide was considered a strong base because it was highly dissociated into ions. An aqueous solution of ammonia, at one time considered to consist of NH_4OH molecules, was classed as a weak base because it dissociated only slightly into positive and negative ions. The dissociation of a weak acid such as acetic acid was represented by the equation

$$CH_3COOH(aq) \rightleftharpoons H^+(aq) + CH_3COO^-(aq) \qquad \textbf{4-1}$$

and the dissociation of the weak base ammonia was formerly represented as

$$NH_4OH(aq) \rightleftharpoons NH_4^+(aq) + OH^-(aq) \qquad \textbf{4-2}$$

2   The Brønsted-Lowry Concept

Brønsted and Lowry independently proposed a system for describing the acidic and basic behavior of substances where hydrogen ions, or protons, were transferred from one substance to another. An acid was defined as a proton donor and a base as a proton acceptor. A strong acid is one which readily donates a proton, and a weak acid is one which has little tendency to donate a proton. Conversely, a strong base readily accepts a proton while a weak base shows little tendency to accept a proton. Simultaneously, with the donation of a proton by an acid, there must also be the acceptance of the proton by a base. The strength of an acid or base will depend upon both factors.

In the Brønsted-Lowry system, the dissociation of a weak acid, such as acetic acid, is represented in aqueous solution by the following equation

$$CH_3COOH(aq) + H_2O(l) \rightleftharpoons H_3O^+(aq) + CH_3COO^-(aq) \qquad \textbf{4-3}$$
$$\quad \text{acid} \qquad\qquad \text{base} \qquad\quad \text{acid} \qquad\qquad \text{base}$$

The acetic acid molecule is an acid because it donates a proton, and the water molecule is a base because it accepts the proton. The strength of acetic acid as an acid depends upon the basic strength of the solvent water. If acetic acid were placed in a solvent having a

50

greater basic strength, the acetic acid would appear to be a stronger acid than it is in water. This has been shown by putting acetic acid into butyl amine with the result that in this solvent acetic acid appears to be as strong an acid as hydrochloric acid. The generalization can be made that the stronger the basic properties of a solvent, the stronger the acids will appear to be; conversely the stronger the acidic properties of a solvent, the stronger the bases will appear to be. The limit is reached when the ionization becomes complete; the acid or base has become a strong electrolyte. In Eq. 4-3 each of the species shown is given the designation *acid* or *base*. The CH_3COOH molecule is designated as an acid and its product, the CH_3COO^- ion, is designated as a base. Such a related pair is known as a *conjugate acid-base pair*. For each substance designated as an acid there must be a conjugate base. The H_3O^+-H_2O pair is also a conjugate acid-base pair.

The species that we define as acids (or bases) under the Brønsted concept may be cations, anions, or neutral molecules. Some examples of each class follow:

Species	*Acids*	*Bases*
Molecules	HCl, CH_3COOH, H_2S H_2Se, H_3PO_4, H_2SO_4, H_2O	NH_3, CH_3NH_2, H_2O $Al(OH)_3$, $Zn(OH)_2$
Cations	H_3O^+, NH_4^+, $[Al(H_2O)_6]^{3+}$ $[Al(H_2O)_5OH]^{2+}$ $[Zn(H_2O)_4]^{2+}$	$[Al(H_2O)_5OH]^{2+}$ $[Fe(H_2O)_4(OH)_2]^+$
Anions	HCO_3^-, HSO_4^-, $H_3IO_6^{2-}$ $H_2PO_4^-$, HPO_4^{2-}, HS^- $[Zn(OH)_3H_2O]^-$	OH^-, $[Al(H_2O)_2(OH)_4^-]$ SO_4^{2-}, HS^-, S^{2-}, CO_3^{2-}, HCO_3^- $[Zn(OH)_4]^{2-}$

Using the Brønsted-Lowry concept the basic character of ammonia can readily be shown by the equation

$$NH_3(aq) + H_2O(l) \rightleftharpoons NH_4^+(aq) + OH^-(aq) \qquad \textbf{4-4}$$

base   acid   acid   base

In the forward reaction, the NH_3 molecule is the proton acceptor and the water molecule is the proton donor.

In Eq. 4-3 the water molecule shows the properties of a base because it accepts a proton; in Eq. 4-4 the water molecule shows the properties of an acid because it donates a proton. A molecule which shows both of these behaviors is called an *ampholyte*. The term is illustrated further by the equation for the ionization of water

$$H_2O(l) + H_2O(l) \rightleftharpoons H_3O^+(aq) + OH^-(aq) \qquad \textbf{4-5}$$

acid   base   acid   base

While it is believed that in aqueous solution the proton is at all times solvated, in this chapter we will talk of the hydrogen ion (written as

H^+) and the hydrogen ion concentration as a convenience. For years H_3O^+ was used to represent the hydrated hydrogen ion, and it now seems probable that $H_9O_4^+$ ions exist through hydrogen bonding of three water molecules to a central H_3O^+ ion.

3   The Lewis Concept

A more generalized concept of acid-base behavior was proposed by G. N. Lewis. Within this concept an acid is defined as an electron-pair acceptor, and a base is defined as an electron-pair donor. The Lewis concept includes those substances considered to be acids and bases under the Brønsted-Lowry concept and it is applicable to numerous other cases. It is particularly useful in describing as acid-base reactions a number of reactions which do not involve protons. Examples of such reactions are

$$(C_2H_5)_3N: + \; BCl_3 \rightleftarrows (C_2H_5)_3N—BCl_3 \qquad \textbf{4-6}$$
$$\text{base} \qquad \text{acid}$$

$$Ni^{2+}(aq) + 4:NH_3(aq) \rightleftarrows Ni(NH_3)_4^{2+}(aq) \qquad \textbf{4-7}$$
$$\text{acid} \qquad \text{base}$$

In the first reaction the boron is electron deficient and accepts an electron pair from the nitrogen. A bond is formed in this process. In the second reaction each of the NH_3 molecules donates a pair of electrons and the Ni^{2+} ion accepts four pairs of electrons. In the process four water molecules are displaced from around the nickel ion. In the reaction ammonia is the base and the nickel ion is the acid.

4–B   DISSOCIATION OF ACIDS AND BASES IN AQUEOUS SOLUTION

1   Activities of Solutes and Solvents

The activity of a *solute* in an ideal solution is the ratio of the actual molar concentration, c_i, to the molar concentration in the standard state, c_i^0, or

$$a_i = c_i/c_i^0 \qquad \text{4-8}$$

For a solute, the standard state, or state of unit activity, is arbitrarily chosen so the concentration, c_i^0, is 1 mole per liter, and for ideal solutions

$$a_i = c_i \qquad \text{4-9}$$

Most real solutions deviate from ideality except at very low concentrations, and Eq. 4-9 is therefore of limited use. The activity of a solute is related to its concentration in any real solution by the equation

$$a_i = y_i c_i/c_i^0 = y_i c_i \qquad \text{4-10}$$

where y_i is a proportionality constant known as the activity coefficient. The activity coefficient approaches unity as the concentration of the solute approaches zero. The activity coefficient serves to correct the analytical concentration of a solute for deviation from ideal behavior.

The activity of the solvent is proportional to the mole fraction of the solvent. The standard state of the solvent is chosen as unit mole fraction. For dilute solutions the mole fraction of the solvent approaches unity and hence its activity approaches unity.

2   Dissociation of Water

Eq. 4-5 shows the dissociation of the solvent water. This equation is often written in the form

$$H_2O(l) \rightleftharpoons H^+(aq) + OH^-(aq) \qquad \text{4-11}$$

The equilibrium expression for this reaction will be

$$K_i^0 = \frac{(a_{H^+})(a_{OH^-})}{(a_{H_2O})} \qquad \text{4-12}$$

This can be simplified because the ion concentrations will be very small and the activity coefficients for hydrogen ion and hydroxide ion will be unity; the activity of the pure solvent water will be unity, and hence one can write

$$K_w = [H^+][OH^-] \, y_+ y_- \cong [H^+][OH^-] \qquad \text{4-13}$$

where $[H^+]$ and $[OH^-]$ are the concentrations of hydrogen and hydroxide ions, and y_+ and y_- are their activity coefficients. The constant K_w is known as the ion product of water.

3   Equilibria Involving Weak Acids

The equilibrium constant for the ionization of a weak acid, such as acetic acid (Eq. 4-3), can be written as

$$K_a{}^0 = \frac{(a_{CH_3COO^-})(a_{H_3O^+})}{(a_{CH_3COOH})(a_{H_2O})} \quad \text{or} \quad \frac{(a_{CH_3COO^-})(a_{H^+})}{(a_{CH_3COOH})(a_{H_2O})} \qquad 4\text{-}14$$

This expression may first be simplified by limiting the case to dilute solutions where $a_{H_2O} \to 1$. The activity of the solute molecules and ions may be written as the product of a concentration term and an activity coefficient term

$$K_a{}^0 = \frac{[CH_3COO^-][H^+]}{[CH_3COOH]} \cdot \frac{y_- y_+}{y_0} \qquad 4\text{-}15$$

y_+, y_-, and y_0 are the molar activity coefficients of the positive, negative, and neutral species respectively. The second term involving the y_i values approaches unity as the solutions become more dilute. In the remainder of this chapter we shall assume the activity coefficients to be equal to unity.

If the ionization constant for an acid is known, the hydrogen ion concentration of a solution of known analytical concentration may be calculated. As an application of the ionization principle let us consider a dilute solution of acetic acid. The equilibrium constant for the ionization reaction may be expressed as

$$K_a = \frac{[H^+][CH_3COO^-]}{[CH_3COOH]} \qquad 4\text{-}16$$

Eq. 4-16 is a relationship which must be satisfied when the various species are present at equilibrium. Since there are three unknowns in Eq. 4-16, one needs at least two other equations without any additional unknowns so that a simultaneous solution to the equations may be obtained. These other equations result from the *electroneutrality condition* and from the *conservation of material*. The total charge on positive ions in the solution will have to be equal to the total charge on negative ions in the solution in order that electrical neutrality be maintained; this is a statement of the *electroneutrality condition*. For acetic acid in an aqueous solution this condition can be expressed by the relation

$$[H^+] = [CH_3COO^-] + [OH^-] \qquad 4\text{-}17$$

There is also a corresponding expression for the *conservation of material*, and for acetic acid solution this is

$$C_t = [CH_3COO^-] + [CH_3COOH] \qquad 4\text{-}18$$

where C_t is the total concentration of the conjugate acid-base pair. We have in Eq. 4-17 introduced a new unknown, the concentration of the hydroxide ion. We now need an additional equation before a solution can be attempted. This additional equation is the ion product of water, Eq. 4-13. Solving Eq. 4-17 for the acetate ion concentration we have

$$[CH_3COO^-] = [H^+] - [OH^-] \qquad \textbf{4-19}$$

and solving Eq. 4-18 for the equilibrium acetic acid concentration we have

$$[CH_3COOH] = C_t - \{[H^+] - [OH^-]\} \qquad \textbf{4-20}$$

When Eqs. 4-19 and 4-20 are substituted in Eq. 4-16, we obtain

$$K_a = \frac{[H^+]\{[H^+] - [OH^-]\}}{(C_t - \{[H^+] - [OH^-]\})} \qquad \textbf{4-21}$$

Substituting for the hydroxide ion concentration from the ion product of water (Eq. 4-13)

$$K_a = \frac{[H^+]\{[H^+] - K_w/[H^+]\}}{(C_t - \{[H^+] - K_w/[H^+]\})} \qquad \textbf{4-22}$$

Eq. 4-22 can be solved for the hydrogen ion concentration; however, one does not usually try to solve such a complicated expression. In most acidic solutions the hydroxide ion concentration term in Eq. 4-21 will be small and can be neglected, giving the equation

$$K_a = \frac{[H^+]^2}{\{C_t - [H^+]\}} \qquad \textbf{4-23}$$

On the condition that the acid is only slightly ionized or not too dilute, this equation can further be simplified. Under either of these conditions the subtracted $[H^+]$ term in the denominator can be neglected

$$K_a = \frac{[H^+]^2}{C_t} \qquad \textbf{4-24}$$

Since the value reported for K_a is 1.75×10^{-5}, let us now calculate the hydrogen ion concentration for acetic acid solutions of various analytical concentrations using the exact Eq. 4-21 and the two approximations 4-23 and 4-24. At $C_t = 0.10$, the result will be almost the same for all three equations because (a) the hydroxide ion concentration is very small, and (b) the hydrogen ion concentration is negligible with respect to C_t. At this analytical concentration, the calculated concentration of hydrogen ion is 1.3×10^{-3} mole per liter.

Now let us look at the results if $C_t = 5.0 \times 10^{-7}$ mole per liter. By Eq. 4-24 the calculated hydrogen ion concentration is 3.0×10^{-6} mole per liter. But this answer can not be correct since it is larger than the analytical concentration of acetic acid. Substituting in Eq. 4-23 and expanding the equation, we obtain

$$[H^+]^2 + 1.75 \times 10^{-5}[H^+] - 8.75 \times 10^{-12} = 0 \qquad \textbf{4-25}$$

The solution of this quadratic equation is $[H^+] = 4.9 \times 10^{-7}$ mole per liter. When Eq. 4-22 is used we get the cubic equation

$$[H^+]^3 + 1.75 \times 10^{-5}[H^2]^+ - (10^{-14} + 8.75 \times 10^{-12})[H^+] \\ - 1.75 \times 10^{-19} = 0 \qquad \textbf{4-26}$$

The solution of this equation by approximate methods is $[H^+] = 5.0 \times 10^{-7}$ mole per liter. The hydrogen ion concentrations at these two acetic acid concentrations along with the similar data for other concentrations using the three equations are shown in Table 4-1. It may be seen from these calculated values that for acetic acid, Eq. 4-24 is useful only for C_t greater than 4×10^{-3} mole per liter. Below that concentration Eq. 4-23 would have to be used and even that equation is not useful at concentrations below about 2×10^{-6} mole per liter. At acetic acid concentrations above 4×10^{-3} mole per liter all three equations give the correct result, so naturally the simplest approximation is used. Concentrations above 4×10^{-3} mole per liter are more often met in practical situations than those below this value.

Table IV-1

Hydrogen Ion Concentration of Solutions of Acetic Acid of Various Concentrations as Calculated from Exact and Approximate Relationships.

Acetic Acid Concentration, C_t	Hydrogen Ion Concentrations		
	Eq. 4-24	Eq. 4-23	Eq. 4-22
$1.0 \times 10^{-1}\ M$	$1.3 \times 10^{-3}\ M$	$1.3 \times 10^{-3}\ M$	$1.3 \times 10^{-3}\ M$
5.0×10^{-2}	9.3×10^{-4}	9.3×10^{-4}	9.3×10^{-4}
1.0×10^{-2}	$\underline{4.2 \times 10^{-4}}$	4.2×10^{-4}	4.2×10^{-4}
5.0×10^{-3}	3.0×10^{-4}	2.9×10^{-4}	2.9×10^{-4}
1.0×10^{-3}	1.3×10^{-4}	1.2×10^{-4}	1.2×10^{-4}
5.0×10^{-4}	9.3×10^{-5}	8.5×10^{-5}	8.5×10^{-5}
1.0×10^{-4}	4.2×10^{-5}	3.4×10^{-5}	3.4×10^{-5}
5.0×10^{-5}	3.0×10^{-5}	2.2×10^{-5}	2.2×10^{-5}
1.0×10^{-5}	1.3×10^{-5}	7.1×10^{-6}	7.1×10^{-6}
5.0×10^{-6}	9.3×10^{-6}	$\underline{4.1 \times 10^{-6}}$	4.1×10^{-6}
1.0×10^{-6}	4.2×10^{-6}	9.5×10^{-7}	9.6×10^{-7}
5.0×10^{-7}	3.0×10^{-6}	4.9×10^{-7}	5.0×10^{-7}
1.0×10^{-7}	1.3×10^{-6}	1.0×10^{-7}	1.6×10^{-7}
5.0×10^{-8}	9.3×10^{-7}	1.0×10^{-7}	1.28×10^{-7}

Values below the line in columns 2 and 3 differ significantly from the correct values of [H$^+$] because the assumptions involved are not valid at low values of C_t.

As the acetic acid solutions become more dilute than that in the last concentration given in Table 4-1, they have a hydrogen ion concentration approaching that of pure water, 1.0×10^{-7} mole per liter, but they can never be below that.

4   Equilibria Involving Weak Bases

For the dissociation of a base such as ammonia a very similar treatment is used. Eq. 4-4 shows the equilibrium existing in a solution of ammonia in water. The equilibrium constant for this reaction is

$$K_b = \frac{[NH_4^+][OH^-]}{[NH_3]} \qquad \text{4-27}$$

The equation stating the condition of electrical neutrality is

$$[H^+] + [NH_4^+] = [OH^-] \qquad \text{4-28}$$

The equation for conservation of material is

$$C_t = [NH_3] + [NH_4^+] \qquad \text{4-29}$$

When Eqs. 4-27, 4-28, and 4-29 are combined they give

$$K_b = \frac{\{[OH^-] - K_w/[OH^-]\}[OH^-]}{C_t - \{[OH^-] - K_w/[OH^-]\}} \qquad \text{4-30}$$

This equation may be simplified, on the assumption that the hydrogen ion concentration is negligibly small in the basic solution, to give

$$K_b = \frac{[OH^-]^2}{\{C_t - [OH^-]\}} \qquad \text{4-31}$$

and, on the additional assumption that the subtracted $[OH^-]$ is negligible with respect to C_t

$$K_b = \frac{[OH^-]^2}{C_t} \qquad \text{4-32}$$

These equations are applicable to the calculation of hydroxide ion concentrations in solutions of ammonia and other weak bases.

5   Conjugate Acid-Base Equilibria

The discussion above can be generalized to handle any weak base or weak acid dissolved in aqueous solution. For example, if a solution of sodium fluoride is under consideration, the equilibrium existing will be

$$\underset{\text{base}}{F^-(aq)} + \underset{\text{acid}}{H_2O(l)} \rightleftharpoons \underset{\text{acid}}{HF(aq)} + \underset{\text{base}}{OH^-(aq)} \qquad \text{4-33}$$

According to the Brønsted-Lowry concept, the fluoride ion acts as a base. The basicity constant would be expressed as

$$K_b = \frac{[HF][OH^-]}{[F^-]} \qquad \textbf{4-34}$$

but in tables of basicity constants one will not find a value listed for fluoride ion or for sodium fluoride. An acidity constant for hydrofluoric acid will be found for the reaction represented by the equation

$$HF(aq) \rightleftharpoons H^+(aq) + F^-(aq) \qquad \textbf{4-35}$$

$$K_a = \frac{[H^+][F^-]}{[HF]} = 6.7 \times 10^{-4} \qquad \textbf{4-36}$$

If we multiply Eq. 4-34 by Eq. 4-36 we get

$$K_a K_b = \frac{[H^+][F^-]}{[HF]} \cdot \frac{[HF][OH^-]}{[F^-]} = [H^+][OH^-] \qquad \textbf{4-37}$$

Thus we can say for the hydrofluoric acid-fluoride ion conjugate acid-base pair that the product of the acidity constant for the hydrofluoric acid and the basicity constant for the fluoride ion is equal to the ion product of water. The relation

$$K_a K_b = K_w \qquad \textbf{4-38}$$

is generally true for any conjugate acid-base pair in aqueous solution.

Let us calculate the hydroxide ion concentration of a 0.05 molar solution of sodium fluoride. From conservation of hydroxide ions

$$[OH^-] = [H^+] + [HF] \cong [HF] \qquad \textbf{4-39}$$

and from the conservation of fluoride ions

$$C_t = [HF] + [F^-] \cong [F^-] \qquad \textbf{4-40}$$

These assumptions are equivalent to the assumptions that were used in deriving Eq. 4-32. Substituting in Eq. 4-32 and solving for $[OH^-]$

$$[OH^-] = \sqrt{\frac{10^{-14} \times 5 \times 10^{-2}}{6.7 \times 10^{-4}}} = 8.6 \times 10^{-7} \ M$$

We can check to see that the use of the approximate equation was justified. The difference between Eq. 4-32 used and the more exact Eq. 4-31 was that the subtracted hydroxide ion concentration was assumed to be negligible. In the case we have here considered

$$[F^-] = C_t - [HF] \cong C_t - [OH^-]$$

$$[F^-] = 0.05 - 8.6 \times 10^{-7} \cong 0.05 \ M$$

The use of the approximate equation is justified.

4–C   LOGARITHMIC EXPRESSION OF HYDROGEN ION CONCENTRATION

Sørensen in 1909 proposed the use of what he called the "hydrogen ion exponent," which has since come to be called the *pH*. The definition of *pH* according to Sørensen is

$$pH = -\log[H^+] \qquad \textbf{4-41}$$

We shall continue to use this definition in this book, although in principle the *pH* is related to the activity of hydrogen ion.

The *pH* concept provides a very convenient way of expressing concentrations that may vary over many orders of magnitude without having to use exponents or a large number of zeros in decimal numbers. For example, suppose one considers the range from 5 molar hydrochloric acid to 5 molar sodium hydroxide. In the first the hydrogen ion concentration is 5 molar and in the second the hydrogen ion concentration is 2×10^{-15}. The *pH* is -0.7 and 14.7, respectively. The *pH* of pure water at 25° is 7.0 because the hydrogen ion concentration is 1.0×10^{-7} mole per liter. The symbol "*p*" followed by some designation is generally used to represent "the negative logarithm of." For example, pK_a represents the negative logarithm of an acidity constant.

4–D   SOLUTION CONTAINING A WEAK ACID AND ITS CONJUGATE BASE

If a solution of a weak acid has some strong base, such as NaOH, added to it, the equation for the reaction is written

$$HA(aq) + OH^-(aq) \rightarrow A^-(aq) + H_2O(l) \qquad \textbf{4-42}$$

If the amount of base added is less than enough to completely neutralize the acid, one has a solution which has both free weak acid, HA, and its conjugate base, A^-, present. The equilibrium constant expression for the ionization of the weak acid must still hold under these conditions

$$K_a = \frac{[H^+][A^-]}{[HA]} \qquad \textbf{4-43}$$

The equation for the condition of electrical neutrality is

$$[H^+] + [Na^+] = [A^-] + [OH^-] \qquad \textbf{4-44}$$

and the equations expressing mass balance are

$$C_t = [HA] + [A^-] \quad \textbf{4-45} \qquad C_b = [Na^+] \quad \textbf{4-46} \qquad C_t = C_a + C_b \quad \textbf{4-47}$$

Solving Eqs. 4-44, 4-45, 4-46, and 4-47 for [HA] and [A$^-$]

$$[A^-] = C_b + [H^+] - [OH^-] \qquad \text{4-48}$$

$$[HA] = C_a - [H^+] + [OH^-] \qquad \text{4-49}$$

Substitution of 4-48 and 4-49 in Eq. 4-43 gives

$$K_a = \frac{[H^+]\{C_b + [H^+] - [OH]^-\}}{\{C_a - [H^+] + [OH^-]\}} \qquad \text{4-50}$$

This equation can be solved for [H$^+$] only with difficulty. Since the hydroxide ion concentration will often be negligible in acidic solution Eq. 4-50 reduces to

$$K_a = \frac{[H^+]\{C_b + [H^+]\}}{\{C_a - [H^+]\}} \qquad \text{4-51}$$

Furthermore, at times when the hydrogen ion concentration is small with respect to the analytical concentrations of acid and added base, Eq. 4-51 reduces to

$$K_a = \frac{[H^+]C_b}{C_a} \qquad \text{4-52a}$$

on rearranging

$$[H^+] = K_a \frac{C_a}{C_b} \qquad \text{4-52b}$$

The *pH* of such a solution is easily calculated from the logarithmic form of Eq. 4-52b, which is sometimes called the Henderson-Hasselbach equation

$$pH = pK_a + \log \frac{C_b}{C_a} \qquad \text{4-53}$$

Similar equations may be derived for solutions of a weak base and its conjugate acid.

4–E   BUFFER SOLUTIONS

The solution discussed in Section 4-D is called a buffer solution because it resists a change in *pH* when base or acid is added. Buffer solutions are very important in equilibria involving acids and bases. Every living cell has conjugate acid-base pairs of various kinds present which tend to maintain a constant *pH*. Many processes involving chemical reactions and many analytical methods require the use of buffered solutions to prevent *pH* changes.

Let us consider by an example how a buffer solution prevents the *pH* from changing. Let us look at a buffer solution having an analytical acetic acid concentration, C_a, of 0.1 M and an analytical sodium acetate concentration, C_b, of 0.1 M. Assuming Eq. 4-53 is applicable, we calculate that this buffer solution has $pH = pK_a$, which is 4.75. If a small quantity of acid is added to this buffer solution it will react with the acetate ion present, and thus there is a slight decrease in the acetate ion concentration and a slight increase of the concentration of acetic acid. The result will be that there is little change in the pH. For example, if we add 1.0 millimole of HCl to a liter of the buffer solution, the new analytical concentrations of the acid and the salt when equilibrium is reestablished will be

$$C_b = 0.10 - 0.001 = 0.099\ M \qquad C_a = 0.10 + 0.001 = 0.101\ M$$

Substituting these values in Eq. 4-53b

$$pH = 4.75 + \log \frac{0.099}{0.101} = 4.74$$

The same quantity of HCl added to a liter of water at $pH = 7$ would cause the pH to change to 3.0.

The term, buffer index, β, has been defined to express the ability of a buffer solution to maintain the pH constant. It is defined as

$$\beta = \frac{dC_b}{dpH} = \frac{dC_b}{d[\text{H}^+]} \frac{d[\text{H}^+]}{dpH} = -\frac{dC_a}{dpH} \qquad \textbf{4-54}$$

When β is large the solution is a good buffer and when it is small the solution is not.

Equation 4-48 may be rewritten

$$C_b = \frac{K_w}{[\text{H}^+]} - [\text{H}^+] + [\text{A}^-] \qquad \textbf{4-55}$$

Equation 4-45 can be solved for [HA] and by substituting in Eq. 4-43 we obtain

$$K_a = \frac{[\text{H}^+][\text{A}^-]}{C_t - [\text{A}^-]} \qquad \textbf{4-56}$$

Solving this for [A⁻] gives

$$[\text{A}^-] = \frac{K_a C_t}{K_a + [\text{H}^+]} \qquad \textbf{4-57}$$

Equation 4-55 when combined with Eq. 4-57 yields

$$C_b = \frac{K_w}{[\text{H}^+]} - [\text{H}^+] + \frac{K_a C_t}{(K_a + [\text{H}^+])} \qquad \textbf{4-58}$$

Differentiating

$$\frac{dC_b}{d[\text{H}^+]} = -\frac{K_w}{[\text{H}^+]^2} - 1 - \frac{K_a C_t}{(K_a + [\text{H}^+])^2} \qquad \textbf{4-59}$$

Since

$$pH = -\log[H^+] = -\frac{1}{2.3}\ln[H^+] \qquad 4\text{-}60$$

$$\frac{dpH}{d[H^+]} = -\frac{1}{2.3[H^+]} \qquad 4\text{-}61$$

Therefore

$$-\frac{dC_a}{dpH} = \frac{dC_b}{dpH} = 2.3\left(\frac{K_w}{[H^+]} + [H^+] + \frac{K_aC_t[H^+]}{(K_a+[H^+])^2}\right) \qquad 4\text{-}62$$

For a strong base, such as NaOH, Eq. 4-62 becomes

$$\beta_{\text{NaOH}} = \frac{2.3K_w}{[H^+]} \qquad 4\text{-}63$$

because the second and third terms become negligibly small as the concentration of sodium hydroxide increases. In a similar manner, for a strong acid, such as HCl, the buffer index becomes equal to $2.3[H^+]$, because terms one and three become negligibly small. For a weak acid the important term is the third term. To calculate the value of β for acetic acid when $[H^+] = K_a$ we have

$$\beta = \frac{2.3K_a^2C_t}{(2K_a)^2} = \frac{2.3C_t}{4} \qquad 4\text{-}64$$

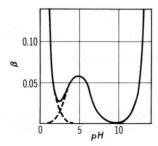

Figure 4-1   Buffer index of $0.1M$ acetate solution *vs. pH*.

Figure 4-1 shows a graph of β as a function of pH for an acetic acid-sodium acetate buffer solution having a total acid-base pair concentration of 0.1 M. The peak at pH 4.75 is the part due to the third term in Eq. 4-62. The increased buffer index due to terms one and three are seen at high pH and low pH, respectively. There is only a small region of overlap between the buffer due to hydrogen ion and that due to the acetic acid-acetate ion buffer.

Let us now calculate the buffer index of the buffer solution containing 0.1 mole of acetic acid and 0.1 mole of sodium acetate per liter and then see how it may be of some practical use. The hydrogen ion concentration of this solution is 1.75×10^{-5} mole/liter and the acidity constant, K_a, is 1.75×10^{-5}. On substitution in Eq. 4-64 for C_t, where $C_t = [HC_2H_3O_2] + [C_2H_3O_2^-] = 0.2$, we obtain

$$\beta = \frac{2.3 \times 0.2}{4} = 0.115$$

This buffer index may be used to calculate the change in pH when 0.001 mole of HCl is added to one liter of our buffer. Changing the dC_b and dpH of Eq. 4-54 to ΔC_b and ΔpH and solving for ΔpH

$$\Delta pH = \Delta C_b/\beta = -0.001/0.115 = -0.009 \; pH \text{ units}$$

or the pH becomes

$$pH = 4.75 - 0.009 = 4.74$$

This is the same answer as obtained earlier in this section by a different method.

4–F GRAPHICAL METHODS OF REPRESENTATION OF IONIZATION EQUILIBRIA

1 Distribution Diagram

We have seen that the acidity constant of a weak acid in a solution is given by the equation

$$K_a = \frac{[H^+][A^-]}{[HA]} \qquad \textbf{4-65}$$

and that the total concentration of the acid and its anion is given by the expression

$$C_t = [HA] + [A^-]$$

We can then express the fraction of the analytical concentration of acid present as the ion $[A^-]$ by α_A. This is identical to the fraction or degree of ionization previously used

$$\alpha_A = \frac{[A^-]}{C_t} = \frac{[A^-]}{[HA] + [A^-]} = \frac{K_a}{K_a + [H^+]} \qquad \textbf{4-66}$$

We will now define α_{HA} as the fraction remaining un-ionized.

$$\alpha_{HA} = \frac{[HA]}{C_t} = \frac{[HA]}{[HA] + [A^-]} = \frac{[H^+]}{K_a + [H^+]} \qquad \textbf{4-67}$$

It should be noted that $\alpha_A + \alpha_{HA} = 1$.

The values of these fractions are a function of the hydrogen ion concentration. Figure 4-2 shows a plot of α_A and α_{HA} as a function of pH for acetic acid which has the acidity constant of 1.75×10^{-5}.

63

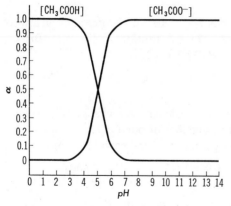

Figure 4-2   Distribution diagram for acetate-acetic acid mixtures.

A 0.02 molar solution of this acid and its anion at $pH = 5$ can be seen from Figure 4-2 to have $\alpha_A = 0.635$ and $\alpha_{HA} = 0.365$. Thus, from Eq. 4-66, $[A^-] = 0.635 \times 0.02 = 0.0127$ mole per liter and from Eq. 4-67, $[HA] = 0.365 \times 0.02 = 0.0073$ mole per liter. In a similar manner the fraction of the species can be read from the graph for any pH. At the midpoint where the two fraction lines cross, $\alpha_A = \alpha_{HA} = 0.50$, $[A^-] = [HA]$, and substituting in Eq. 4-65, $[H^+] = K_a$, and $pH = pK_a$.

2   The Logarithmic Concentration Diagram

A logarithmic concentration diagram is prepared by plotting the logarithm of the concentrations of the various species versus pH. First, the curves for hydrogen and hydroxide ions are plotted. Since $pH = -\log[H^+]$ the curve for hydrogen ion will be a straight line which has a slope of -1. When $\log[H^+] = 0$, $pH = 0$, and when $\log[H^+] = -7$, the $pH = 7$. A straight line is drawn through these two points as shown in Figure 4-3.

The line for the hydroxide ion will be a straight line of slope $+1$, because $pH = 14 - \log[OH^-]$. When $\log[OH^-] = -7$, $pH = 7$ and when $\log[OH^-] = 0$, $pH = 14$. A straight line is drawn through these two points.

To obtain a plot for the variation of the concentration of the weak acid, HA, as a function of pH, the following procedure is employed. Assuming that $pK_a = 6.00$ and $C_t = 2.00 \times 10^{-2}$ mole per liter, a point is placed on the graph at ×, with coordinates, $\log C_t = -1.7$ and $pH = pK_a = 6$ as shown in Figure 4-3. The logarithmic equation of Eq. 4-65 may be written

$$pK_a = pH - \log[A^-] + \log[HA] \qquad \text{4-68}$$

64

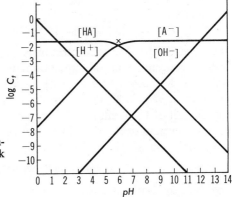

Figure 4-3   Logarithmic concentration diagram for weak acid, $pK_a = 6.0$.

We see by examining Figure 4-2 that at pH values considerably less than pK_a, most of the material will be present as HA; therefore, Eq. 4-68 may be rewritten

$$\log[A^-] = pH - pK_a + \log C_t \qquad\qquad \textbf{4-69}$$

From the point where $pH = 0$ to a point 1.5 pH units to the left of the point ×, the log[HA] is represented by a horizontal line at log $C = -1.7$, and log[A$^-$] is represented by a line of slope of $+1$. Both lines would run directly through the point × if extended. At pH values considerably larger than pK_a, it may be seen from Figure 4-2 that most of the material is present as A$^-$, and Eq. 4-68 may be rewritten

$$\log[HA] = pK_a - pH + \log C_t \qquad\qquad \textbf{4-70}$$

At all pH values 1.5 pH units or more to the right of the point × , the log[A$^-$] is represented by a horizontal line at log $C_t = -1.7$ and log[HA] is represented by a straight line of slope -1. Both of these lines would run directly through the point × if extended. The two line sections representing the log[A$^-$] must connect at some point as must the two line sections representing the log[HA]. From our argument in the last section, log[A$^-$] = log[HA] at the point where $pH = pK_a$, and at this point $[A^-] = [HA] = C_t/2$. The logarithm of $C_t/2$ is equal to (log $C_t - 0.30$). This means that the two curves will cross at 0.30 units below the point × on the graph.

Figure 4-3 provides a graphical method of solving the algebraic equations. Directly from the graph one can read the answer to two simple problems. (1) What is the pH of a 0.02 M solution of the weak acid which has $pK_a = 6.0$? The statement of electrical neutrality in this solution is

$$[H^+] = [A^-] + [OH^-] \qquad \qquad 4\text{-}71$$

and since the OH^- ion concentration is very much lower than the other two ion concentrations this equation reduces to $[H^+] = [A^-]$. The *pH* is that at the point where $\log[H^+] = \log[A^-]$, i.e., the crossing of the two lines at *pH* = 3.85. (2) What is the *pH* of a 0.02 *M* solution of the sodium salt of the weak acid having $pK_a = 6.0$, or whose anion has a basicity constant of 10^{-8}? The statement expressing balance of protons in this solution is

$$[HA] + [H^+] = [OH^-] \qquad \qquad 4\text{-}72$$

and since the H^+ ion concentration is very much lower than the other two ion concentrations this equation reduces to $[HA] = [OH^-]$. The *pH* is that at the point where $\log[HA] = \log[OH^-]$, i.e., the crossing of the two lines at *pH* = 9.15.

The lines representing $\log[H^+]$ and $\log[OH^-]$ must remain fixed on the diagram, but as the concentration of a given acid changes the point × will move vertically along the pK_a coordinate. Figure 4-4 is a logarithmic diagram containing the information for acetic acid at four different concentrations (0.1 *M*, 1×10^{-3} *M*, 1×10^{-5} *M*, and 5×10^{-7} *M*). The *pH* values for each of these solutions may be read where the curves representing $[CH_3COO^-]$ for the solutions cross the +1 slope line representing $[H^+]$. The *pH* of the four solutions can be read from the graph in Figure 4-4 to be 2.85, 3.90, 5.15, and 6.30. These are exactly the same as the results listed in Table 4-1 for the same concentrations.

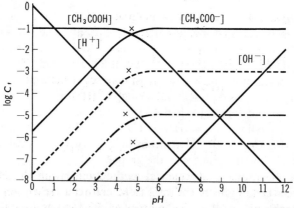

Figure 4-4   Logarithmic concentration diagram for acetic acid (—— 0.1*M*, - - - - $10^{-3}M$, —·—·— $10^{-5}M$, —··—··— $5 \times 10^{-7}M$).

Such logarithmic diagrams are often very useful in getting approximate answers to problems without doing any numerical work. When the graph is used as a reference, a quick check can be made to find if the numerical answers obtained by calculation are reasonable.

4–G   POLYPROTIC ACIDS

Some acids donate more than a single proton. The protons are donated in steps and each step constitutes an equilibrium with its own acidity constant. An example of a diprotic acid is malonic acid, $HOOCCH_2COOH$, which we shall designate as H_2M for purposes of saving space. Malonic acid ionizes as follows:

$$H_2M(aq) \rightleftharpoons H^+(aq) + HM^-(aq) \qquad pK_1 = 2.82 \qquad \textbf{4-73}$$

$$HM^-(aq) \rightleftharpoons H^+(aq) + M^{2-}(aq) \qquad pK_2 = 5.66 \qquad \textbf{4-74}$$

1   The Distribution Diagram

The fractions of the various species present may be calculated for a polyprotic acid at a known *pH* in the same way as for a monoprotic acid. Let us construct a distribution diagram for malonic acid, for which the acidity constants are represented by the following equations:

$$K_1 = \frac{[H^+][HM^-]}{[H_2M]} = 1.5 \times 10^{-3} \qquad \textbf{4-75}$$

$$K_2 = \frac{[H^+][M^{2-}]}{[HM^-]} = 2.2 \times 10^{-6} \qquad \textbf{4-76}$$

The statement of conservation of malonic acid is

$$C_t = [H_2M] + [HM^-] + [M^{2-}] \qquad \textbf{4-77}$$

Substitution in this from Eqs. 4-75 and 4-76

$$C_t = [H_2M] + \frac{K_1[H_2M]}{[H^+]} + \frac{K_1K_2[H_2M]}{[H^+]^2} \qquad \textbf{4-78}$$

Factoring out common terms

$$C_t = \frac{[H_2M]}{[H^+]^2} ([H^+]^2 + K_1[H^+] + K_1K_2) \qquad \textbf{4-79}$$

The fraction of the acid which is undissociated will be given the symbol α_0, the fraction of the total H_2M present as HM^- ion will be given the symbol α_1, and the fraction of the total H_2M present as M^{2-} ion will be given the symbol α_2.

67

$$\alpha_0 = \frac{[H_2M]}{C_t} = \frac{[H^+]^2}{([H^+]^2 + K_1[H^+] + K_1K_2)} \qquad \textbf{4-80}$$

$$\alpha_1 = \frac{[HM^-]}{C_t} = \frac{K_1[H^+]}{([H^+]^2 + K_1[H^+] + K_1K_2)} \qquad \textbf{4-81}$$

$$\alpha_2 = \frac{[M^{2-}]}{C_t} = \frac{K_1K_2}{([H^+]^2 + K_1[H^+] + K_1K_2)} \qquad \textbf{4-82}$$

A graph of the values calculated for malonic acid is shown in Figure 4-5, and at $pH = 5$ it may be seen that $\alpha_0 = 0.01$, $\alpha_1 = 0.81$, and $\alpha_2 = 0.18$. Again it is obvious that $\alpha_0 + \alpha_1 + \alpha_2 = 1$. If the solution has an analytical malonic acid concentration of 0.10 mole per liter at pH 5, the actual concentrations of the species would be

$$[H_2M] = 0.01 \times 0.10 = 0.001 \ M$$
$$[HM^-] = 0.81 \times 0.10 = 0.081 \ M$$
$$[M^{2-}] = 0.18 \times 0.10 = 0.018 \ M$$

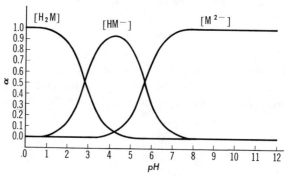

Figure 4-5 Distribution diagram for malonic acid-malonate mixtures *vs. pH.*

By looking at the line in Figure 4-5 that represents α_1, it can be seen that the $[HM^-]$ never reaches 100%. At the maximum of this curve there is 93% HM^- at $pH = 4.24$. At this pH there is also 3.5% H_2M and 3.5% M^{2-}.

2 Logarithmic Concentration Diagram

A logarithmic concentration diagram for a polyprotic acid can be presented in a manner very similar to that for a monoprotic acid. Figure 4-6 is such a diagram for malonic acid at 0.1 mole per liter. There are seen to be a point × with coordinates $\log C_t = -1$ and $pH = pK_1 = 2.82$, and a point × with coordinates $\log C_t = -1$ and $pH = pK_2 = 5.66$. All of the lines have limiting slopes of $+1$, 0, or -1 except those representing $\log[M^{2-}]$ at pH values less than

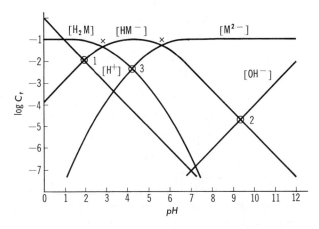

Figure 4-6 Log concentration diagram for malonic acid.

2.82 and $\log[H_2M]$ at *pH* values greater than 5.66. The logarithmic equations may be written for Eqs. 4-75 and 4-76

$$pK_1 = pH - \log[HM^-] + \log[H_2M] \qquad \textbf{4-83}$$
$$pK_2 = pH - \log[M^{2-}] + \log[HM^-] \qquad \textbf{4-84}$$

Solving for log $[HM^-]$ in Eq. 4-83 and substituting in Eq. 4-84

$$pK_2 = 2\,pH + pK_1 + \log[H_2M] - \log[M^{2-}] \qquad \textbf{4-85}$$

If one considers Eq. 4-85 at the point where $\log[H_2M] = \log C_t$, it becomes

$$\log[M^{2-}] = 2\,pH + pK_1 - pK_2 + \log C_t \qquad \textbf{4-86}$$

If one considers Eq. 4-85 at the point where $\log[M^{2-}] = \log C_t$

$$\log[H_2M] = -2\,pH + pK_2 - pK_1 + \log C_t \qquad \textbf{4-87}$$

Thus, at *pH* values below 2.82 the curve for $\log[M^{2-}]$ will have a slope of $+2$ and at *pH* values above 5.66 the curve for $\log[H_2M]$ will have a slope of -2.

From Figure 4-6, one can directly read the answer to three problems. (1) What is the *pH* of a 0.10 *M* solution of malonic acid? (2) What is the *pH* of a 0.10 *M* solution of disodium malonate? (3) What is the *pH* of a 0.10 *M* solution of sodium hydrogen malonate?

First let us solve algebraically. (1) To determine the *pH* of a 0.10 *M* solution of malonic acid, we begin with the condition of electrical neutrality which is

$$[H^+] = [HM^-] + 2[M^{2-}] + [OH^-] \qquad \textbf{4-88}$$

69

However, both $[M^{2-}]$ and $[OH^-]$ are extremely small, so the solution is where $[H^+] = [HM^-]$, and substitution in Eq. 4-75 gives

$$\frac{[H^+]^2}{C_t - [H^+]} = 1.5 \times 10^{-3} \qquad \textbf{4-89}$$

The result is

$$[H^+] = 1.2 \times 10^{-2} \, M$$

$$pH = 1.92$$

An identical answer can be seen to be obtained by taking the line crossing at point 1 in Figure 4-6.

(2) To obtain the pH of a 0.10 M solution of disodium malonate, we first assume that it is ionized completely and write the statement of conservation of protons

$$[OH^-] = [HM^-] + [H^+] + 2[H_2M] \qquad \textbf{4-90}$$

but the concentrations of $[H^+]$ and $[H_2M]$ will be negligibly small so

$$[OH^-] = [HM^-]$$

On substitution in Eq. 4-32 we obtain

$$[OH^-] = \sqrt{\frac{10^{-14} \times 0.10}{2.2 \times 10^{-6}}} = 2.1 \times 10^{-5} \, M \qquad \textbf{4-91}$$

$$pH = 9.33$$

Again this answer can be read from Figure 4-6 at point 2.

In order to find the solution to question (3) we must derive a relationship for the hydrogen ion concentration of an acid salt. The compound sodium hydrogen malonate is first a salt, and we will assume that it has ionized completely to give Na^+ and HM^- ions. The HM^- ion can either give up a proton by ionization or can accept a proton

$$HM^-(aq) \rightleftharpoons H^+(aq) + M^{2-}(aq)$$

$$HM^-(aq) + H^+(aq) \rightleftharpoons H_2M(aq)$$

The equilibrium constants for these equilibria are

$$\frac{[H^+][M^{2-}]}{[HM^-]} = K_2 \qquad \textbf{4-92}$$

$$\frac{[H_2M]}{[H^+][HM^-]} = \frac{1}{K_1} \qquad \textbf{4-93}$$

The statement of electrical neutrality is

$$[H^+] + [Na^+] = [HM^-] + 2[M^{2-}] + [OH^-] \qquad \textbf{4-94}$$

70

The statement of conservation of malonate is

$$C_t = [H_2M] + [HM^-] + [M^{2-}] \qquad \textbf{4-95}$$

Noting that $C_t = [Na^+]$ and combining Eqs. 4-94 and 4-95, we obtain

$$[H^+] = [M^{2-}] + [OH^-] - [H_2M] \qquad \textbf{4-96}$$

Substituting in Eq. 4-96 from Eqs. 4-92, 4-93, and the ion product of water, the resulting equation is

$$[H^+] = \frac{K_2[HM^-]}{[H^+]} + \frac{K_w}{[H^+]} - \frac{[H^+][HM^-]}{K_1} \qquad \textbf{4-97}$$

Multiplying through by $[H^+]K_1$ and solving for $[H^+]$ we obtain

$$[H^+] = \sqrt{\frac{K_1K_2[HM^-] + K_1K_w}{K_1 + [HM^-]}} \qquad \textbf{4-98}$$

This simplifies under the condition that $K_1 \ll [HM^-]$ and $K_w \ll K_2[HM^-]$ to give

$$[H^+] = \sqrt{K_1K_2} \qquad \textbf{4-99}$$

This is identical to assuming in Eq. 4-96 that $[H^+]$ and $[OH^-]$ are negligible and that $[M^{2-}] = [H_2M]$

$$[H^+] = \sqrt{1.3 \times 10^{-3} \times 2.2 \times 10^{-6}} = 5.7 \times 10^{-5} \, M$$

$$pH = 4.24$$

This value may also be seen from inspection of Figure 4-6 at point 3.

4-H   COMPLEX IONS

A simple metal ion which has bonded directly to it other charged or noncharged groups is known as a *complex ion*. The bonded groups are known as *ligands*. The bonding of the ligand often may be considered to arise from the sharing of an electron pair furnished by the ligand. The formation of this bond may be considered to be an acid-base reaction according to the Lewis concept.

In aqueous solution, there is no such entity as a simple metal ion in the uncomplexed state, since there are always a number of co-ordinated solvent molecules. There is a large amount of experimental evidence to support the premise that metal ions have a particular number of strongly bonded water molecules in aqueous solution. For example, aqueous solutions of $Cr(NO_3)_3$ are known to contain $Cr(H_2O)_6{}^{3+}$ ions.

A simple case of the formation of a complex ion can be represented by the equation

$$M^{2+}(aq) + L^-(aq) \rightleftharpoons ML^+(aq) \qquad \textbf{4-100}$$

$$K_f = \frac{[ML^+]}{[M^{2+}][L^-]} \qquad \textbf{4-101}$$

The subsequent calculations are not considerably different from those involved in acid-base equilibria. Let us calculate the concentration of M^{2+} and ML^+ in a solution with analytical concentrations of $M^{2+} = 0.01\ M$ and $L^- = 0.10\ M$, where the formation constant for the complex ion ML^+ is 1000. The exact statements of the conditions for the conservation of M and L are

$$0.010 = [M^{2+}] + [ML^+]$$

$$0.10 = [L^-] + [ML^+]$$

Substitution in Eq. 4-101 leads to

$$1000 = \frac{0.010 - [M^{2+}]}{[M^{2+}](0.10 - 0.01 + [M^{2+}])}$$

This can be solved approximately by noting that $[M^{2+}]$ is probably (because of the magnitude of the equilibrium constant) going to be very small compared to 0.01. Making this assumption, we obtain

$$[M^{2+}] = \frac{0.010}{1000 \times 0.090} = 1.1 \times 10^{-4}M$$

$$[ML^+] = 0.010 - 1.1 \times 10^{-4} = 9.9 \times 10^{-3}\ M$$

Let us next consider in some detail a system which is representative of the formation of many complex ions in aqueous solution. When a soluble silver salt is introduced into an aqueous ammonia-ammonium ion solution, the ammonia reacts with the silver ion to form complexes and the equilibria established are

$$Ag^+(aq) + NH_3(aq) \rightleftharpoons Ag(NH_3)^+(aq) \qquad K_1 = \frac{[AgNH_3^+]}{[Ag^+][NH_3]} \qquad \textbf{4-102}$$

$$Ag(NH_3)^+(aq) + NH_3(aq) \rightleftharpoons Ag(NH_3)_2^+(aq)$$

$$K_2 = \frac{[Ag(NH_3)_2^+]}{[Ag(NH_3)^+][NH_3]} \qquad \textbf{4-103}$$

$$NH_4^+(aq) + H_2O \rightleftharpoons NH_3(aq) + H_3O^+(aq) \qquad K_a = \frac{[NH_3][H^+]}{[NH_4^+]} \qquad \textbf{4-104}$$

$$2\,H_2O(l) \rightleftharpoons H_3O^+(aq) + OH^-(aq) \qquad K_w = [H^+][OH^-] = 1.0 \times 10^{-14}$$
$$\textbf{4-105}$$

Because ammonia has combined with silver ion, the equilibrium represented by Eq. 4-104 lies further to the right than it would in the absence of silver ion. There has therefore been an increase in acidity and a decrease in the *pH* of the solution. In 1941, Professor Jannik Bjerrum published details of a method for determining the formation constants of complex ions formed between metal ions and ligands which behaved as bases in aqueous solution. Bjerrum's method is based on determining the *pH* of equilibrium systems. A set of data obtained by Bjerrum for the silver-ammonia system is presented in Table 4-2.

Table IV-2

pH Measurements of Ammoniacal Silver Nitrate Solutions at 30°C.

$C_{Ag} = 2.00 \times 10^{-2}$ *M* $C_H = 2.0000$ *M*

C_{NH_3}	pH	C_{NH_3}	pH
2.00502	4.937	2.02512	5.607
2.01004	5.177	2.03012	5.760
2.01504	5.336	2.03514	5.962
2.02006	5.470	2.05022	7.001

Bjerrum defined a quantity called the *formation function*, $\bar{n}$, which represents the average number of bound ligands per metal ion. The formation function is given by the equation

$$\bar{n} = \frac{[AgNH_3^+] + 2[Ag(NH_3)_2^+]}{C_{Ag}} \qquad \text{4-106}$$

where C_{Ag} represents the total analytical concentration of silver ion. The formation function, $\bar{n}$, should increase as the concentration of ammonia increases. It is possible to relate the two mathematically as shown in the succeeding paragraphs.

First, let us write mass balances for the various substances present. For silver

$$C_{Ag} = [Ag^+] + [AgNH_3^+] + [Ag(NH_3)_2^+] \qquad \text{4-107}$$

For ammonia

$$C_{NH_3} = [NH_3] + [NH_4^+] + [Ag(NH_3)^+] + 2[Ag(NH_3)_2^+] \qquad \text{4-108}$$

---

* Data calculated from J. Bjerrum, *Metal Ammine Formation in Aqueous Solution*, P. Haase and Sons, Copenhagen, 1941.

C_{NH_3} represents the analytical concentration of ammonia added to the system. For hydrogen

$$C_H = [H^+] + [NH_4^+] - [OH^-] = [H^+] + [NH_4^+] - \frac{K_w}{[H^+]} \qquad \text{4-109}$$

C_H represents the analytical concentration of acid added to the system.

The concentration of free ligand (NH_3) is easily determined by a measurement of the *pH* of the solution. From the acidity constant for ammonia and Eq. 4-109

$$[NH_3] = \frac{[NH_4^+]K_a}{[H^+]} = \frac{K_a}{[H^+]} \left\{ C_H - [H^+] + \frac{K_w}{[H^+]} \right\} \qquad \text{4-110}$$

Next, an equation to determine $\bar{n}$ is required. Combining Eqs. 4-108 and 4-110 we obtain

$$\bar{n} = \frac{C_{NH_3} - [NH_3] - [NH_4^+]}{C_{Ag}} \qquad \text{4-111}$$

Substituting for $[NH_3]$ from Eq. 4-110 and $[NH_4^+]$ from Eq. 4-109, we obtain

$$\bar{n} = \frac{C_{NH_3} - \left(\frac{K_a}{[H^+]} + 1 \right) \left(C_H - [H^+] + \frac{K_w}{[H^+]} \right)}{C_{Ag}} \qquad \text{4-112}$$

From a measurement of the *pH* of the solution, $\bar{n}$ may be calculated if C_{NH_3}, C_H, C_{Ag}, K_a, and K_w are known. The first three quantities are established at the choice of the experimenter; K_a and K_w are known equilibrium constants.

Finally, the relationship between $\bar{n}$ and $[NH_3]$ must be established. Returning to the definition of $\bar{n}$, we can substitute for the concentrations of the complex silver species from Eqs. 4-102 and 4-103 and cancelling $[Ag^+]$ between numerator and denominator, we obtain

$$\bar{n} = \frac{K_1[NH_3] + 2K_1K_2[NH_3]^2}{1 + K_1[NH_3] + K_1K_2[NH_3]^2} \qquad \text{4-113}$$

This equation can be solved for K_1 and rewritten in the from

$$K_1 = \frac{\bar{n}}{[NH_3](1 - \bar{n}) \left\{ 1 + \frac{(2 - \bar{n})}{(1 - \bar{n})} K_2[NH_3] \right\}} \qquad \text{4-114}$$

Taking the logarithm of both sides

$$\log K_1 = \log \frac{\bar{n}}{(1 - \bar{n})} - \log[NH_3] - \log \left\{ 1 + \frac{(2 - \bar{n})}{(1 - \bar{n})} K_2[NH_3] \right\} \qquad \text{4-115}$$

74

When $\bar{n}$ is less than 1, the principal species present will be silver ion and $Ag(NH_3)^+$. Therefore we may drop the last term of Eq. 4-115 and write

$$\log K_1 = \log \frac{\bar{n}}{1-\bar{n}} + pNH_3 \qquad \textbf{4-116}$$

When $\bar{n} = 1/2$, $\log \bar{n}/(1 - \bar{n}) = 1$, and $\log K_1 = pNH_3$. A plot of $\bar{n}$ *vs.* pNH_3 provides a convenient graphical method of determining K_1 as shown in Figure 4-7. For $\bar{n} = 1/2$, $pNH_3 = 3.82$ and therefore $K_1 = 6.6 \times 10^3$.

Similarly Eq. 4-113 may be written in the form

$$\log K_2 = \log \frac{(\bar{n}-1)}{(2-\bar{n})} - \log[NH_3] + \log\left\{\frac{\bar{n}}{K_1[NH_3](\bar{n}-1)} + 1\right\} \qquad \textbf{4-117}$$

In the region of $\bar{n} = 3/2$, the last term may be neglected, and

$$\log K_2 = \log \frac{(\bar{n}-1)}{(2-\bar{n})} - \log[NH_3] \qquad \textbf{4-118}$$

When $\bar{n} = 3/2$, $\log K_2 = pNH_3$. From Figure 4-7, we see $pNH_3 = 3.22$ at $\bar{n} = 3/2$. Therefore, $K_2 = 1.66 \times 10^3$.

It should be observed from Figure 4-7 that the average number of ligands per metal ion, $\bar{n}$, approaches 2 as a maximum value when the concentration of ammonia increases.

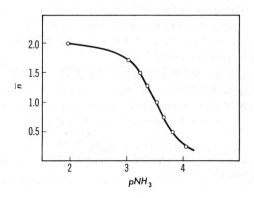

Figure 4-7   Formation curve for diamminesilver(I) at 15°C.

Problems

4-1   Calculate the concentration of all species present and the *pH* in each of the following solutions:

(a) A 0.047 *M* solution of acetic acid.

(b) A 2.5×10^{-3} *M* solution of a weak acid with $K_a = 2.4 \times 10^{-5}$.

(c) A 3.4×10^{-3} M solution of the sodium salt of the acid in (b).

(d) A mixture of equal volumes of the solutions in (b) and (c).

(e) Solution (d) diluted to 100 times its original volume.

(f) A 0.050 M solution of a weak base, $K_b = 2.5 \times 10^{-5}$.

(g) A 25 ml sample of solution (f) which has added to it 20 ml of 0.050 M hydrochloric acid.

(h) A 0.050 M solution of a diprotic acid for which $K_1 = 2.2 \times 10^{-4}$ and $K_2 = 4.2 \times 10^{-7}$.

(i) A 25 ml sample of solution (h) which has added to it 25 ml of 0.050 M sodium hydroxide.

(j) A 25 ml sample of solution (h) which has added to it 50 ml of 0.050 M sodium hydroxide.

4-2   Calculate the fraction ionized, α, for solutions of acetic acid which have concentrations:

(a) 0.10 M

(b) 0.05 M

(c) 0.002 M

(d) 0.0004 M

4-3   For the values below, calculate the fraction of un-ionized acid, α_{HA}, and the fraction of anion, α_{A^-}, for a weak acid-salt of weak acid solution where $K_a = 5.8 \times 10^{-5}$.

(a) 3.49

(b) 4.49

(c) 6.05

4-4   (a) Calculate the buffer index of a solution containing 0.08 mole of a weak acid and 0.08 mole of its sodium salt in one liter if $K_a = 3.7 \times 10^{-5}$.

(b) Calculate the pH of this buffer solution.

(c) Calculate the pH that solution (a) will have after the addition of 3 millimoles of NaOH per liter of solution.

4-5   For ethylenediamine, $NH_2CH_2CH_2NH_2$, $pK_{1b} = 4.07$ and $pK_{2b} = 7.15$. What are the fractions and concentrations of each species present if the 0.020 M solution has enough hydrochloric acid added to it to give a pH of 5.85?

4-6   Calculate the concentration of each species present if a solution has an analytical concentration of 1.0×10^{-3} M Zn^{2+} when the equilibrium concentration of NH_3 is 0.050 M, $\log K_1 = 2.27$, $\log K_2 = 2.34$, $\log K_3 = 2.40$, and $\log K_4 = 2.05$.

4-7   The ligand 2,2′-bipyridine (abbr. L) forms a complex with the formula AgL_2^{+}. The value of $\beta_2 = 7.1 \times 10^6$. What are the concentrations of all species when a liter of 0.0010 M $AgNO_3$ has 0.02 mole of 2,2′-bipyridine added to it?

4-8   Using the data in Table 4-2, calculate pNH_3 and $\bar{n}$ for each of the values of C_{NH_3}. Make a plot of $\bar{n}$ *vs.* pNH_3 and evaluate K_1 and K_2. Compare your values with those reported in this chapter.

5–A SOLUBILITY AND THE SOLUBILITY PRODUCT CONSTANT OF IONIC COMPOUNDS

A slightly soluble solid ionic dissolves spontaneously in a solvent until some definite concentration of the solute exists in equilibrium with the solid at a given temperature and pressure. The concentration of the solute under these conditions is known as its solubility. The question arises as to why a solid dissolves in a liquid at all. As with other chemical systems at constant temperature and pressure, the system tends to achieve the minimum possible free energy, and therefore a solid dissolves until that state is attained. Generally, the entropy change favors dissolution because the solution has a higher entropy than the sum of the entropies of the pure solid and pure liquid. The enthalpy change may or may not be favorable; this depends on the differences between the energy required to separate ions of the solid and the energy released through hydration of the ions. Once equilibrium is established, the free energy of the solid solute is equal to the free energy of the solute in the solution.

For the dissolution of one mole of the salt MX in an infinite volume of a solution of MX of some particular concentration as shown by the equation

$$MX(s) \rightleftharpoons M^+(aq) + X^-(aq) \qquad \text{5-1}$$

the free energy change is given by the equation

$$\Delta G = \mu_{M^+} + \mu_{X^-} - \mu_{MX} \qquad \text{5-2}$$

On defining the chemical potentials as in Eq. 3-7 and activities as in Eq. 4-8, we obtain

$$\Delta G = [\mu^0_{M^+} + RT \ln a_{M^+}] + [\mu^0_{X^-} + RT \ln a_{X^-}] - [\mu^0_{MX} + RT \ln a_{MX}]$$

$$\text{5-3}$$

On substituting and collecting terms, we obtain

$$\Delta G = \mu^0_{M^+} + \mu^0_{X^-} - \mu^0_{MX} + RT \ln(a_{M^+})(a_{X^-})/(a_{MX}) \qquad \text{5-4}$$

Since

$$\Delta G^0 = \mu^0{}_{M^+} + \mu^0{}_{X^-} - \mu^0{}_{MX} \qquad \textbf{5-5}$$

we can substitute in the preceding equation to obtain the result

$$\Delta G = \Delta G^0 + RT \ln (a_{M^+})(a_{X^-})/(a_{MX}) \qquad \textbf{5-6}$$

For a system at equilibrium at constant temperature and pressure, ΔG is zero and therefore

$$\Delta G^0 = -RT \ln (a_{M^+})(a_{X^-})/(a_{MX}) \qquad \textbf{5-7}$$

Since ΔG^0, R, and T are constant terms, the logarithmic term must also be constant. Further, the activity of a pure solid in its standard state is unity and $a_{MX} = 1$. On substituting we obtain

$$\Delta G^0 = -RT \ln (a_{M^+})(a_{X^-}) \qquad \textbf{5-8}$$

This logarithmic term is also constant and is known as the *solubility product constant, $K_s{}^0$*. It is defined by the equation

$$K_s{}^0 = (a_{M^+})(a_{X^-}) \qquad \textbf{5-9}$$

The significance of this equation is that the product of the activities of the solute ions must be constant when a solid is in equilibrium with its solution. By combining equations it follows that

$$\Delta G^0 = -RT \ln K_s{}^0 \qquad \textbf{5-10}$$

ΔG^0 represents the change in free energy when one mole of solid MX dissolves to form one mole of $M^+(aq)$ and one mole of $X^-(aq)$, both at unit activity.

For the dissolution of a more complex salt as shown by the equation

$$M_pX_q(s) \rightleftharpoons pM^+(aq) + qX^-(aq) \qquad \textbf{5-11}$$

the solubility product constant is given by

$$K_s{}^0 = (a_{M^+})^p(a_{X^-})^q \qquad \textbf{5-12}$$

ΔG^0 for this reaction represents the free energy change for the formation of p moles of $M^+(aq)$ and q moles of $X^-(aq)$ in their standard states from 1 mole of solid M_pX_q in its standard state.

The dissolution of the slightly soluble salt silver nitrite is shown by the equation

$$AgNO_2(s) \rightleftharpoons Ag^+(aq) + NO_2{}^-(aq) \qquad \textbf{5-13}$$

Using Eq. 4-10 to relate activities to concentration, we may write

$$K_s{}^0 = (a_{Ag^+})(a_{NO_2^-}) = [Ag^+][NO_2{}^-]y_+y_- \qquad \textbf{5-14}$$

The product of the concentrations of the ions in equilibrium with the solid may be defined as

$$K_s = [Ag^+][NO_2^-] \qquad \textbf{5-15}$$

and is sometimes called the *concentration solubility product*. Combining 5-14 and 5-15, we obtain

$$K_s{}^0 = K_s y_+ y_- \qquad \textbf{5-16}$$

For dilute real solutions, the activity coefficients may be assumed to be approximately unity, and hence, K_s should have approximately constant values for different solutions. In Table 5-1 are tabulated some experimental data for solutions which were obtained by dissolving and equilibrating solid silver nitrite in either an aqueous solution of silver nitrate or an aqueous solution of potassium nitrite. Values of K_s have been calculated and are included in Table 5-1.

There are some interesting aspects of the data presented in Table 5-1. First, as the concentration of silver ion increases, the concentration of nitrite ion decreases. This is seen by comparing the ion concentrations for Experiments 2–4 with those of Experiment 1. Le Chatelier's principle predicts this behavior. If excess silver nitrate is added to a saturated solution of silver nitrite, then a reaction must occur which tends to consume the added silver ion. This can only occur if silver ion and nitrite ion combine to form insoluble silver nitrite. When the new equilibrium is established, the nitrite ion concentration will be less than that originally present while the silver ion concentration will be greater. Second, as predicted by Eq. 5-15, the values of K_s for the various solutions are approximately constant over the limited concentration range presented. As will be

Table V-1

Solubility of silver nitrite in aqueous solutions of silver nitrate or potassium nitrite at 25°C.

Expt.	[AgNO₃]	[KNO₂]	[AgNO₂]	[Ag⁺]	[NO₂⁻]	K_s
1	—	—	$2.69 \times 10^{-2}M$	$2.69 \times 10^{-2}M$	$2.69 \times 10^{-2}M$	7.24×10^{-4}
2	$2.58 \times 10^{-3}M$	—	2.60×10^{-2}	2.86×10^{-2}	2.60×10^{-2}	7.44×10^{-4}
3	5.88×10^{-3}	—	2.44×10^{-2}	3.03×10^{-2}	2.44×10^{-2}	7.39×10^{-4}
4	1.177×10^{-2}	—	2.24×10^{-2}	3.42×10^{-2}	2.24×10^{-2}	7.66×10^{-4}
5	—	$2.58 \times 10^{-3}M$	2.59×10^{-2}	2.59×10^{-2}	2.85×10^{-2}	7.38×10^{-4}
6	—	5.88×10^{-3}	2.49×10^{-2}	2.49×10^{-2}	3.08×10^{-2}	7.67×10^{-4}

Average value of K_s $(7.46 \pm 0.13) \times 10^{-4}$

seen in Table 5-3 (p. 87), a more constant value of the solubility product constant is obtained if values for activity coefficients are included rather than assuming them to be unity.

An important use of the solubility product constant is in the determination of whether a precipitate should form on mixing two solutions. It is perhaps somewhat easier to provide an answer to the opposite, but related question, "Will a solid dissolve in a solution of given composition?" Consider the dissolution of a solid as represented by Eq. 5-1. The free energy change, ΔG, for such a process is the difference between the free energies of formation of one mole of each of the ions at some arbitrary activity and the free energy of one mole of the solid. From consideration of Eqs. 5-6 and 5-7, it can be shown that

$$\Delta G = -RT \ln K_s{}^0 + RT \ln (a_{M^+})(a_{X^-}) \qquad \textbf{5-17}$$

The term $Q_s{}^0$ can be defined as before to have the same form as the equilibrium constant (solubility product constant), but to represent the actual existing concentrations (or activities) in the system. Hence $Q_s{}^0 = ([M^+][X^-]y_+y_-)$ and with the assumption that the activities of the ions in solution can be replaced by their concentrations, we can write

$$\Delta G \cong -RT \ln K_s + RT \ln Q_s \qquad \textbf{5-18}$$

When solid silver nitrite is first placed in water, there is no detectable concentration of silver ion or nitrite ion, and hence $Q_s = 0$. ΔG then equals $-\infty$, and some finite amount of solid silver nitrite should dissolve. As the concentrations of silver and nitrite ions increase, Q_s increases and eventually equals K_s. At this point, ΔG is 0 and equilibrium is established. No further increase in the concentration of solute occurs.

To answer the question of whether a precipitate forms on mixing two solutions, one first needs to know the concentrations of the species present in the solution after mixing. These can be calculated if the concentrations and volumes of the solutions to be mixed are known. From such information Q_s can be calculated. If Q_s is less than K_s, no precipitate forms because ΔG for the dissolution reaction would still be negative, and, if any solid happened to be present, it would dissolve spontaneously. If Q_s is greater than K_s, ΔG for the dissolution reaction would be positive. However, for the reverse reaction, ΔG would be negative. Therefore, if Q_s is greater than K_s, precipitation should occur. If Q_s happens to be numerically equal to K_s, $\Delta G = 0$ and the system is at equilibrium. No solid would appear to dissolve, and none would appear to form.

It should be emphasized that there is a limitation to predictions of precipitation from thermodynamic considerations. One can only predict that precipitation will or will not occur when equilibrium is established. One cannot use thermodynamics to predict how rapidly equilibrium will be attained.

5–B   CALCULATIONS OF K_s^0 AND THE SOLUBILITY FROM STANDARD FREE ENERGIES OF FORMATION

In Table 5-2 are recorded values for the standard free energies of formation, enthalpies of formation, and entropies of aqueous ions and solutes. The changes in the thermodynamic quantities resulting from a change of the state of a system may be calculated for a solubility reaction in the same manner as described earlier for other reactions. For example, let us calculate the solubility of silver iodide in aqueous solution at $298°K$. The equation for the chemical reaction is

$$AgI(s) \rightleftharpoons Ag^+(aq) + I^-(aq) \qquad \textbf{5-19}$$

Then

$$\Delta G^0 = \Delta G^0_{f(Ag^+)} + \Delta G^0_{f(I^-)} - \Delta G^0_{f(AgI)} \qquad \textbf{5-20}$$

$$\Delta G^0 = 18.43 + (-12.35) - (-15.85)$$

$$\Delta G^0 = 21.93 \text{ kcal}$$

Since

$$\Delta G^0 = -RT \ln K_s^0$$

$$\log K_s^0 = -\frac{21.93}{1.364} = -16.08$$

$$K_s^0 = 8.3 \times 10^{-17}$$

An experimental value of 8.5×10^{-17} obtained from a direct radiochemical determination of the solubility is in good agreement with this calculated value. Values determined by other methods are also within a few per cent.

Let us also evaluate ΔH^0 and ΔS^0 for the dissolution of silver iodide.

$$\Delta H^0 = \Delta H^0_{f(Ag^+)} + \Delta H^0_{f(I^-)} - \Delta H^0_{f(AgI)} \qquad \textbf{5-21}$$

$$\Delta H^0 = 25.31 + (-13.37) - (-14.91)$$

$$\Delta H^0 = +26.85 \text{ kcal}$$

Table V-2

*Standard Thermodynamic Functions for the Formation of the Species Indicated in Aqueous Solution at 298°K.**

Formula	$\Delta G^0{}_f$ (kcal)	$\Delta H^0{}_f$ (kcal)	S^0 (e.u.)
H^+	0	0	0
Ni^{2+}	−11.53	−15.3	—
Cu^{2+}	15.53	15.39	−23.6
Ba^{2+}	−134.0	−128.67	3.
Ag^+	18.430	25.31	17.67
Tl^+	−7.755	1.38	30.4
$NH_4{}^+$	−19.00	−31.74	26.97
NH_3	−6.36	−19.32	—
HNO_2	−12.82	−28.4	—
$NO_2{}^-$	−8.25	−25.4	29.9
$NO_3{}^-$	−26.43	−49.372	35.0
H_2CO_3	−149.00	−167.0	45.7
$HCO_3{}^-$	−140.31	−165.18	22.7
$CO_3{}^{2-}$	−126.22	−161.63	−12.7
CH_3COO^-	−89.02	−116.843	—
CH_3COOH	−95.51	−116.743	—
I^-	−12.35	−13.37	26.14
$Ag(NH_3)_2{}^+$	−4.16	−26.724	57.8
$Cu(NH_3)_4{}^{2+}$	−40.8	−79.9	—
$Ni(NH_3)_4{}^{2+}$	−46.9	—	—
HCl	−31.350	−40.023	13.2
Cl^-	−31.350	−40.023	13.2
$SO_4{}^{2-}$	−177.34	−216.90	4.1
OH^-	−37.595	−54.595	−2.519

* Data from W. M. Latimer, *Oxidation Potentials* (1952), Prentice Hall, New York.

and

$$\Delta S^0 = S^0{}_{(Ag^+)} + S^0{}_{(I^-)} - S^0{}_{(AgI)}$$

$$\Delta S^0 = 17.67 + 26.14 - 27.3$$

$$\Delta S^0 = +16.51 \text{ e.u.}$$

5-22

Using the calculated value of $K_s{}^0$, let us calculate the solubility of silver iodide in water at 298°K. Let the molar solubility be S. If we assume that neither silver ion nor iodide ion undergoes hydrolysis, we determine from a consideration of the conservation of charge that when equilibrium is established

$$[Ag^+] = [I^-] = S$$

Assuming ideal solutions, i.e., $y_+ = y_- = 1$,

$$K_s^0 = [Ag^+][I^-] = S \times S = S^2 \qquad\qquad \textbf{5-23}$$
$$S = \sqrt{K_s^0} = \sqrt{8.3 \times 10^{-18}} = \sqrt{83 \times 10^{-18}}$$
$$S = 9.1 \times 10^{-9} \text{ mole/liter}$$

This relatively low solubility for a salt such as AgI is less than might be expected. Let us look at the thermodynamic changes to see if a low solubility is reasonable. ΔG^0 is $+21.93$ kcal. For the conversion of one mole of solid silver iodide to one mole of aqueous silver ion and one mole of aqueous iodide ion, each at unit activity, the free energy change is highly positive. The value of ΔH^0 for the process is also very positive, $+26.85$ kcal. This means a large amount of energy must be supplied to make the reaction go. The energy holding the ions in the crystal (the lattice energy) must be large compared to the hydration energy. While the entropy is positive and thus favorable, the product $T\Delta S^0$ is only 4.92 kcal and is not sufficiently positive to offset the positive value of ΔH^0. With this information on ΔH^0 and $T\Delta S^0$, the very low solubility for silver iodide in water is not unreasonable.

5–C   EFFECT OF STRONG ELECTROLYTES ON SOLUBILITY

1   Inert Electrolytes

Often in the study of solutions of a salt MX, other electrolytes are present. If these electrolytes do not interact chemically or have no ion in common with the salt under investigation, the electrolytes are said to be *inert electrolytes*. The effect of an inert electrolyte on the properties of MX is usually small and often neglected. Eq. 5-15 predicts that no effect at all should be observed if the solution shows ideal behavior, *i.e.*, if the activities of the M^+ and X^- ions are not affected by the inert electrolyte. This situation is in fact approached only in very dilute solutions and is truly attained only as the total inert electrolyte concentration goes to zero.

For any real solutions there are deviations from ideality. These deviations arise from the interaction of a given ion with its neighbors. On a time average a given ion will be surrounded by an "ion atmosphere" of opposite sign because of the electrostatic attraction and repulsion of ions. A positive ion will have a greater probability of being located in a negatively charged ion atmosphere than in a positively charged one. Similarly, a negative ion will tend to be in a positively charged ion atmosphere. The net charge of the atmosphere is equal in magnitude but opposite in sign to the charge of the central ion. The result of the ion atmosphere effect is that the positive and negative ions are not completely free to act independently of each other and their chemical activities are less than they should be. Generally, for solutions less concentrated than one molar, the deviations from ideality decrease as concentrations decrease. This behavior is a result of the increased average distance between ions in the more dilute solutions. The farther removed an ion is from the ions constituting its atmosphere, the less will be the interaction between them. The charge density is greater at the central ion and decreases with increasing distance.

The immediate result of this type of deviation from nonideal behavior is that the activity of an ion is no longer equal to its concentration, and to relate the two, the concept of the *activity coefficient* is introduced. The activity coefficient is the proportionality constant y_i in Eq. 4-10. This is simply the ratio of the activity of an ion to its concentration, and for aqueous solutions whose total concentration is less than about one molar, y_i is usually less than unity. In other words, the activity of an ion is less than its concentration.

The effect of an increasing inert electrolyte concentration on the solubility of silver bromate is represented by the upper curve in Figure 5-1. Here the solubility of silver bromate increases slightly as the concentration of potassium nitrate increases. The solubility product for silver bromate is given by the equation

$$K_s{}^0 = (a_{Ag^+})(a_{BrO_3^-}) = [Ag^+][BrO_3^-]y_+y_- = S^2 y_+ y_- \qquad \textbf{5-24}$$

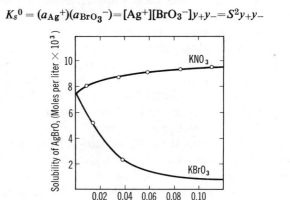

Figure 5-1 Solubility at 25°C of silver bromate in aqueous solutions of KNO_3 and $KBrO_3$ as a function of ionic strength. Curves plotted from calculated data; small circles represent experimental data.

Since $K_s{}^0$ must in fact remain constant, and since the concentrations of silver and bromate ions are observed to increase with increasing inert electrolyte concentrations, the activity coefficients must simultaneously decrease. This behavior is typical of many slightly soluble electrolytes in the presence of inert electrolytes.

The effects of inert electrolytes on the activities of other electrolytes were recognized by A. A. Noyes, N. Bjerrum, R. Milner and other early workers in the field. Professor G. N. Lewis of the University of California pointed out that the activity of an electrolyte MX varies with the total electrolyte concentration of the solution and with the charge type of the inert electrolyte. Inert electrolytes having ions of higher charge affect the activity of MX more than 1 : 1 electrolytes such as NaCl. To correlate these effects, a function known as the ionic strength, I, was defined by Lewis as shown by the equation

$$I = 1/2 \sum_i C_i Z_i{}^2 \qquad \textbf{5-25}$$

where C_i is the concentration of an ion and Z_i is its charge. It appears that the activity coefficient of a salt MX is constant for solutions of given ionic strength regardless of the type of the electrolytes contributing to the total ionic strength.

Let us compare the ionic strengths of different types of salts at the same total concentration by calculating I for solutions of NaCl, $CaCl_2$, and $CaSO_4$ whose molarities are M moles per liter.

For NaCl, $I = 1/2\{[Na^+](Z_{Na^+})^2 + [Cl^-](Z_{Cl^-})^2\}$
$$= 1/2(M \times 1^2 + M \times 1^2) = 1M$$

For $CaCl_2$, $I = 1/2\{[Ca^{2+}](Z_{Ca^{2+}})^2 + [Cl^-](Z_{Cl^-})^2\}$
$$= 1/2(M \times 2^2 + 2M \times 1^2) = 3M$$

For $CaSO_4$, $I = 1/2\{[Ca^{2+}](Z_{Ca^{2+}})^2 + [SO_4{}^{2-}](Z_{SO_4{}^{2+}})^2\}$
$$= 1/2(M \times 2^2 + M \times 2^2) = 4M$$

From this it is seen that a high charge type electrolyte will cause a solution to have a higher ionic strength than the same concentration of a lower charge type.

The most successful theoretical approach to the activity coefficient problem has been that of Professors Peter Debye and W. Hückel. These two scientists derived for the activity coefficient of an ion in aqueous solution at 298°K the relationship

$$\log y_i = -0.509 \, Z_i{}^2 \, \sqrt{I} \qquad \textbf{5-26}$$

This equation, which has proven to be extremely useful for calculating activity coefficients of electrolytes in very dilute solutions, is known as the Debye-Hückel Limiting Law. It has been found experimentally that activity coefficients do not decrease as rapidly with increasing ionic strength as predicted by this equation.

To extend the range of ionic strengths for which activity coefficients may be calculated, several modifications of Eq. 5-26 have been proposed. Two of the more useful are

$$\log y_i = -0.509\, Z_i{}^2 \left(\frac{\sqrt{I}}{1 + \sqrt{I}}\right) \qquad \textbf{5-27}$$

and

$$\log y_i = -0.509\, Z_i{}^2 \left(\frac{\sqrt{I}}{1 + \sqrt{I}} - 0.2\, I\right) \qquad \textbf{5-28}$$

These equations are applicable to ionic strengths of about 0.1 with an accuracy of a few per cent. Above this ionic strength, their reliability decreases. Eq. 5-28 generally gives a better representation of activity coefficients than do the other two.

Let us calculate $K_s{}^0$ for silver bromate using the experimental data recorded in Table 5-3 for the solubility of silver bromate in lithium perchlorate solutions. One must first calculate the ionic strength I from Eq. 5-25, assuming that both silver bromate and lithium perchlorate are strong electrolytes and are completely dissociated in aqueous solution. The activity coefficients can be estimated from Eq. 5-28. Note that y_+ and y_- have the same numerical values since the ions have charges of the same magnitude. The product of the equilibrium concentrations of the ions, K_s, and the product of the equilibrium activities of the ions, $K_s{}^0$, have both been listed in Table 5-3.

The noteworthy features of the information in Table 5-3 are the following. First, as I increases from 0.0081 to 0.1095, K_s increases by about 40% while $K_s{}^0$ is constant with an average deviation of only $\pm 0.6\%$. Second, as the ionic strength of the solution increases the deviation from ideality increases and the calculated activity coefficients decrease.

2   Electrolytes With a Common Ion

The solubility of silver bromate in water was established to be $8.09 \times 10^{-3}\ M$ when no added electrolyte was present. The equation for the equilibrium involved is

$$\text{AgBrO}_3(s) \rightleftharpoons \text{Ag}^+(aq) + \text{BrO}_3{}^-(aq) \qquad \textbf{5-29}$$

From the preceding discussion, it would be predicted that the solubility would increase if an inert electrolyte were added because of ionic strength effects on the activities of silver and bromate ions. Some electrolytes are not inert and have an ion in common with a slightly soluble compound. In the case of silver bromate any silver salt or any bromate salt would have an ion in common. If either is added to a water-silver bromate system where solubility equilibrium has been established, the molar solubility of silver bromate is reduced. This is as predicted by Le Chatelier's principle. Consider, for example, the addition of solid potassium bromate which increases the bromate ion concentration of the solution. A reaction must occur which consumes some of the added bromate ion. This can occur only when solid silver bromate is formed with the resultant decrease of the silver ion concentration. Generally, the addition of a soluble electrolyte having an ion in common with a slightly soluble electrolyte causes a reduction in the equilibrium concentration of the noncommon ion of the slightly soluble electrolyte. This is an example of what is known as the *common ion effect*.

In Figure 5-1 the lower curve shows the solubility of silver bromate in aqueous solutions of potassium bromate. Note that there is a decrease in solubility

Table V-3

Solubility of Silver Bromate in Aqueous Lithium Perchlorate Solutions at 25°C.

$[LiClO_4]$	$[AgBrO_3]$	I	y_+ or y_-	$y_+ y_-$	K_s	K_s^0
0.000M	$8.09 \times 10^{-3} M$	8.09×10^{-3}	0.910	0.828	6.54×10^{-5}	5.42×10^{-5}
0.025	8.73×10^{-3}	3.37×10^{-2}	0.839	0.704	7.62×10^{-5}	5.36×10^{-5}
0.050	9.09×10^{-3}	5.91×10^{-2}	0.806	0.650	8.26×10^{-5}	5.37×10^{-5}
0.075	9.25×10^{-3}	8.44×10^{-2}	0.783	0.613	8.74×10^{-5}	5.36×10^{-5}
0.100	9.52×10^{-3}	10.95×10^{-2}	0.773	0.598	9.06×10^{-5}	5.42×10^{-5}
					Average K_s^0	$(5.39 \pm .03) \times 10^{-5}$

Data from R. W. Ramette and E. A. Dratz, *J. Phys. Chem.*, **67**, 940 (1963).

with increasing ionic strength which is caused by increasing the concentration of the salt with the common ion.

Solubility data for silver bromate in aqueous solutions of potassium bromate are recorded in Table 5-4. Values of activity coefficients were calculated using Eq. 5-28. Values of K_s and K_s^0, are also recorded. Note that values of K_s^0 increase only slightly over the range of ionic strengths represented, while K_s increases by a greater margin. The values of K_s^0 are comparable to those reported in Table 5-3.

Table V-4

Solubility of $AgBrO_3$ in Aqueous Potassium Bromate Solutions at 25°C

[KBrO$_3$]	[AgBrO$_3$]	I	y_+ or y_-	y_+y_-	K_s	K_s^0
0.000M	$8.09 \times 10^{-3}M$	8.09×10^{-3}	.910	.828	5.39×10^{-5}	5.42×10^{-5}
8.50×10^{-3}	5.19×10^{-3}	1.37×10^{-2}	.887	.787	7.10×10^{-5}	5.59×10^{-5}
3.46×10^{-2}	2.27×10^{-3}	3.69×10^{-2}	.835	.697	8.37×10^{-5}	5.83×10^{-5}

We have already calculated (see Eq. 5-23) the solubility of AgI in water to be 9.1×10^{-9} M. Let us now calculate the molar solubility of silver iodide in a 1.00×10^{-4} M solution of potassium iodide. In this instance the common ion effect is of importance.

Let $X =$ molar solubility of silver iodide at equilibrium. Then $[Ag^+] = X$ because every mole of silver iodide in solution produces one silver ion and one iodide ion. The concentration of iodide ion is equal to the amount from silver iodide plus the amount from potassium iodide. $[I^-] = (X + 1.00 \times 10^{-4})$ M. Assuming that the solutions are sufficiently dilute so that activity coefficients may be assumed to be unity, we can write for the solubility product

$$K_s^0 \cong K_s = [Ag^+][I^-] \qquad \textbf{5-30}$$
$$8.3 \times 10^{-17} = [X][X + 1.00 \times 10^{-4}] \qquad \textbf{5-31a}$$
$$8.3 \times 10^{-17} = X^2 + 1.00 \times 10^{-4}X \qquad \textbf{5-31b}$$

Equation 5-31b can be solved exactly using the general solution to the quadratic equation, or it can be approximated by dropping the X^2 term. This also is equivalent to assuming that X is small compared to 1.00×10^{-4} in Eq. 5-31a. Either procedure leads to the equation

$$8.3 \times 10^{-17} = 1.00 \times 10^{-4}X$$
$$X = 8.3 \times 10^{-13} \ M$$

Indeed, X is small compared to 1.00×10^{-4} and the approximation is justified. The solubility of silver iodide in 1.00×10^{-4} M potassium iodide solution is 8.3×10^{-13} M. This is almost a factor of 10^4 less than the solubility of silver iodide in pure water.

5–D   EFFECT OF COMPLEXING AGENTS AND pH ON THE SOLUBILITY

1   Common Ions Which form Complexes with the Metal Ion

Until now, we have explicitly assumed that the anions present in the solutions do not form complex ions with the metal ions present. This is an underlying assumption to the earlier statement that strong electrolytes are completely dissociated in aqueous solution. If this is true, then the molar solubility, S, of thallous chloride in aqueous potassium chloride should be given by the equation

$$K_s^0 = (a_{Tl^+})(a_{Cl^-}) = [Tl^+][Cl^-]y_+y_- = (S)(S + [Cl^-])y_+y_- \qquad \textbf{5-32}$$

In the case $S \ll [Cl^-]$ this reduces to

$$S = \frac{K_s^0}{[Cl^-]y_+y_-} \qquad \textbf{5-33}$$

Equation 5-33 is of the form $y = bx$, and a plot of y *vs.* x should be a straight line of slope b passing through the origin. Therefore a plot of S *vs.* $1/[Cl^-]y_+y_-$ should be a straight line of slope K_s^0 passing through the origin. Figure 5-2 shows a plot of the solubility of thallous chloride in aqueous potassium chloride solutions. Over a large range of concentration, the plot is linear, but it obviously does not go through the origin. At values of $1/[Cl^-]y_+y_-$, less than about 10, there is a noticeable deviation from linearity. There must therefore be something questionable about the basic assumption of complete dissociation in the case of TlCl.

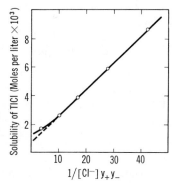

Figure 5-2   Solubility at 25°C of thallous chloride in aqueous potassium chloride *vs.* $1/[Cl^-]y_+y_-$.

Let us see how one can explain the plot in Figure 5-2. First, for the solubility equilibrium represented by the equation

$$TlCl(s) \rightleftharpoons Tl^+(aq) + Cl^-(aq) \qquad \textbf{5-34}$$

the solubility product constant is

$$K_s^0 = [Tl^+][Cl^-]y_+y_- \qquad \text{5-35}$$

If undissociated species, or complex ions, are formed by thallous ion and chloride ion, the following equations may be used to represent the equilibria and equilibrium conditions involved.

$$Tl^+(aq) + Cl^-(aq) \rightleftharpoons TlCl(aq) \qquad \text{5-36}$$

$$\beta_1^0 = \frac{[TlCl(aq)]}{[Tl^+][Cl^-]} \frac{y_0}{y_+y_-} \qquad \text{5-37}$$

Where y_0 is the activity coefficient of the undissociated $TlCl(aq)$ in solution. Activity coefficients of uncharged species are usually very close to unity and are usually assumed to be unity.

$$Tl^+(aq) + 2\,Cl^-(aq) \rightleftharpoons TlCl_2^-(aq) \qquad \text{5-38}$$

$$\beta_2^0 = \frac{[TlCl^{2-}]}{[Tl^+][Cl_2^-]} \frac{y_-}{y_+y_{-2}} \qquad \text{5-39}$$

The total concentration of thallium in the solution is the solubility S, and the equation for the conservation of thallium in the aqueous phase may be written as

$$S = [Tl^+] + [TlCl(aq)] + [TlCl_2^-] + \cdots \qquad \text{5-40}$$

From Eqs. 5-37 and 5-38 we may substitute for $TlCl(aq)$ and $TlCl_2^-$ in Eq. 5-40

$$S = [Tl^+] + \beta_1^0[Tl^+][Cl^-]y_+y_- + \beta_2^0[Tl^+][Cl^-]^2 y_+y_- + \cdots \qquad \text{5-41}$$

Substituting for Tl^+ from Eq. 5-35 and cancelling where possible, we obtain

$$S = \frac{K_s^0}{[Cl^-]y_+y_-} + \beta_1^0 K_s^0 + \beta_2^0 K_s^0[Cl^-] + \cdots \qquad \text{5-42}$$

If we assume for the moment that the undissociated species present in solution is $TlCl(aq)$ and that chloride complexes having a higher chloride to thallium ratio than $1:1$ are not present, Eq. 5-42 simplifies to

$$S = \frac{K_s^0}{[Cl^-]y_+y_-} + \beta_1^0 K_s^0 \qquad \text{5-43}$$

The variables here are S and $1/[Cl^-]y_+y_-$. Equation 5-43 is that of a straight line with a slope of K_s^0 and an intercept of $\beta_1^0 K_s^0$ at $1/[Cl^-]y_+y_- = 0$. The plot of S *vs.* $1/[Cl^-]y_+y_-$ in Figure 5-2 is indeed a straight line over a considerable range. The extrapolated intercept is 7.5×10^{-4} and the slope is 1.78×10^{-4}. Therefore $K_s^0 = 1.78 \times 10^{-4}$

and
$$\beta_1{}^0 K_s{}^0 = 7.5 \times 10^{-4} \qquad \textbf{5-44}$$

$$\beta_1{}^0 = \frac{7.5 \times 10^{-4}}{K_s{}^0} = \frac{7.5 \times 10^{-4}}{1.78 \times 10^{-4}} = 4.2$$

The upward curvature to the plot at high concentrations of chloride ion may be due to formation of $TlCl_2{}^-(aq)$, or, as some investigators believe, it may be due to the failure of the activity coefficient equations to yield accurate values of y_i.

In the total effect of potassium chloride on the solubility of thallous chloride, there are three factors to be considered. First, as the concentration of potassium chloride increases, the ionic strength of the solution increases and the activity coefficients decrease. This tends to cause an increase in the solubility. Second, since potassium chloride has an ion in common with thallous chloride, the effect of increased chloride ion concentration is to reduce the solubility. Third, since the chloride ion tends to form complexes with the thallous ion, there is a tendency for the solubility of thallous chloride to be increased by the presence of potassium chloride. The actual solubility of thallous chloride in any potassium chloride solution will depend on a combination of all three factors. The solubility is described quantitatively by Eq. 5-42 and can be calculated if the solubility product constant and the formation constants of the complex ions are known.

2   Effect of Other Complexing Agents on Solubility

The presence of ions or molecules which form complexes with either one or both of the ions of a slightly soluble electrolyte will cause the solubility of the latter to increase. For example, consider the case of silver chloride in water.

$$AgCl(s) \rightleftharpoons Ag^+(aq) + Cl^-(aq) \qquad \textbf{5-45}$$

$$K_s{}^0 = [Ag^+][Cl^-]y_+ y_- = 1.78 \times 10^{-1}{}^0 \qquad \textbf{5-46}$$

The addition of ammonia causes silver ion to be converted to silver ammonia complex ions as shown by the equations

$$Ag^+(aq) + NH_3(aq) \rightleftharpoons Ag(NH_3)^+(aq) \qquad \textbf{5-47}$$

$$\beta_1{}^0 = \frac{[Ag(NH_3)^+]}{[Ag^+][NH_3]} = 2.33 \times 10^3 \qquad \textbf{5-48}$$

$$Ag^+(aq) + 2\,NH_3(aq) \rightleftharpoons Ag(NH_3)_2{}^+(aq) \qquad \textbf{5-49}$$

$$\beta_2{}^0 = \frac{[Ag(NH_3)_2{}^+]}{[Ag^+][NH_3]^2} = 1.61 \times 10^7 \qquad \textbf{5-50}$$

Hence, silver chloride should be more soluble in aqueous ammonia than it is in water alone because of the removal of silver ion from the solubility equilibrium.

Using the values of the solubility product constant of silver chloride and the formation constants of the silver ammonia complexes, let us calculate the solubility of silver chloride in water and also in a solution whose ammonia concentration at equilibrium is 0.1000 M. For simplicity, let it be assumed that the solutions behave ideally and that activities are numerically equal to the concentrations of solutes. The molar solubility in water in the absence of complexing agents is given by the equation

$$S \cong \sqrt{K_s^0} = \sqrt{1.78 \times 10^{-10}} = 1.33 \times 10^{-5} \, M$$

When solid silver chloride is equilibrated with an ammonia solution whose analytical concentration is 1.024×10^{-1} mole per liter, the concentration of ammonia molecules is only 0.1000 mole per liter. Let us calculate the solubility of silver chloride in such a solution and also calculate the concentrations of NH_4^+, Ag^+, $Ag(NH_3)^+$, $Ag(NH_3)_2^+$, H^+ and OH^-. Again let S = molar solubility of silver chloride. Then, since chloride is not associated with any other species present

$$S = [Cl^-] \tag{5-51}$$

S also must equal the total concentration of silver in the solution. From a mass balance on silver

$$S = [Ag^+] + [AgNH_3^+] + [Ag(NH_3)_2^+] \tag{5-52}$$

Substituting from Eqs. 5-48 and 5-50

$$S = [Ag^+] + \beta_1^0[Ag^+][NH_3] + \beta_2^0[Ag^+][NH_3]^2 \tag{5-53}$$
$$S = [Ag^+]\{1 + \beta_1^0[NH_3] + \beta_2^0[NH_3]^2\} \tag{5-54}$$

But, since chloride ion and silver ion are in equilibrium with solid silver chloride, we can combine Eqs. 5-46 and 5-51 with Eq. 5-54. Remembering that we have assumed activities to be equal to concentrations, we obtain

$$S^2 = K_s^0\{1 + \beta_1^0[NH_3] + \beta_2^0[NH_3]^2\} \tag{5-55}$$

On substituting numerical values the result is

$$S^2 = 1.78 \times 10^{-10} \, \{1 + 2.33 \times 10^3 \times 1.00 \times 10^{-1} +$$
$$1.61 \times 10^7 \times (1.00 \times 10^{-1})^2\}$$

$$S = 5.36 \times 10^{-3} \, M = [Cl^-]$$

$$[Ag^+] = K_s^0/[Cl^-] = 1.78 \times 10^{-10}/5.36 \times 10^{-3} = 3.32 \times 10^{-8} \, M$$

$$[AgNH_3^+] = \beta_1^0[NH_3][Ag^+]$$
$$= 2.33 \times 10^3 \times 1.00 \times 10^{-1} \times 3.32 \times 10^{-8} = 7.50 \times 10^{-6} \, M$$

$$[Ag(NH_3)_2^+] = \beta_2^0[NH_3]^2[Ag^+]$$
$$= 1.61 \times 10^7 \times (1.00 \times 10^{-1})^2 \times 3.32 \times 10^{-8} = 5.35 \times 10^{-3} \, M$$

To obtain the concentration of ammonium ion, we must use the charge balance

$$[Ag^+] + [AgNH_3^+] + [Ag(NH_3)_2^+] + [H^+] + [NH_4^+] = [OH^-] + [Cl^-]$$

5-56

The total concentration of silver ions equals total concentration of chloride ion and these terms will drop out of Eq. 5-56. Therefore, we obtain

$$[NH_4^+] + [H^+] = [OH^-]$$ **5-57**

On rearranging we obtain

$$[NH_4^+] = [OH^-] - [H^+]$$ **5-58**

In basic solutions, $[OH^-]$ will be much greater than $[H^+]$ and as an approximation we may write

$$[NH_4^+] = [OH^-]$$ **5-59**

Substituting in the basicity constant for ammonia and extracting the square root yields the equation

$$[NH_4^+] = \sqrt{K_b^0 \times [NH_3]}$$ **5-60**

For a solution with an equilibrium concentration of $[NH_3] = 1.00 \times 10^{-1} M$

$$[NH_4^+] = \sqrt{1.78 \times 10^{-6}} = 1.33 \times 10^{-3} M$$
$$[H^+] = K_u/[OH^-] = 7.51 \times 10^{-12} M$$

To see if our calculations are correct, let us substitute numerical values into Eq. 5-56.

$$3.32 \times 10^{-8} + 7.50 \times 10^{-6} + 5.35 \times 10^{-3} + 7.51 \times 10^{-12} +$$
$$1.33 \times 10^{-3} = 1.33 \times 10^{-3} + 5.36 \times 10^{-3}$$
$$6.69 \times 10^{-3} = 6.69 \times 10^{-3}$$

It should be observed that the solute species present in order of decreasing concentrations are

$$[Cl^-] > [Ag(NH_3)_2^+] > [OH^-] \cong [NH_4^+] > [AgNH_3^+] > [Ag^+] > [H^+]$$

The solubility of silver chloride may be calculated for any equilibrium concentration of ammonia by the method just outlined. The results of a series of such calculations are shown in Figure 5-3 where the logarithm of S is plotted against the logarithm of the total of all forms of ammonia in the solution. Below concentrations where log C is -4, increasing ammonia concentration has little effect on the solubility of silver chloride because only a very small fraction of silver

93

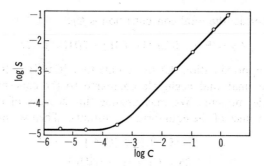

Figure 5-3 Variation of the logarithm of solubility of silver chloride *vs.* logarithm of total ammonia concentration. (Data from *Int. Crit. Tables*, Vol. VII, p. 269–270.)

ion in the aqueous phase is complexed. Between log C values of -4 and -3, appreciable concentrations of complexed silver ion are present and the solubility begins to increase. Above values of log C $= -3$, the solubility of silver chloride increases sharply with increasing ammonia concentration as was predicted earlier.

3   Effect of *pH* on Solubility of Slightly Soluble Electrolytes

On the saturation of water with solid calcium fluoride, among the several equilibria eventually established are those represented by the equations

$$CaF_2(s) \rightleftharpoons Ca^{2+}(aq) + 2F^-(aq) \qquad \textbf{5-61}$$

$$K_s{}^0 = (a_{Ca^{2+}})(a_{F^-})^2 = 3.4 \times 10^{-11} \qquad \textbf{5-62}$$

$$H^+(aq) + F^-(aq) \rightleftharpoons HF(aq) \qquad \textbf{5-63}$$

$$\frac{1}{K_a{}^0} = \frac{(a_{HF})}{(a_{H^+})(a_{F^-})} = 1.48 \times 10^3 \qquad \textbf{5-64}$$

$$HF(aq) + F^-(aq) \rightleftharpoons HF_2{}^-(aq) \qquad \textbf{5-65}$$

$$K_2{}^0 = \frac{(a_{HF_2^-})}{(a_{HF})(a_{F^-})} = 3.90 \qquad \textbf{5-66}$$

$$Ca^{2+}(aq) + F^-(aq) \rightleftharpoons CaF^+(aq) \qquad \textbf{5-67}$$

$$K_3{}^0 = \frac{(a_{CaF^+})}{(a_{Ca^{2+}})(a_{F^-})} \leq 10 \qquad \textbf{5-68}$$

$$Ca^{2+}(aq) + OH^-(aq) \rightleftharpoons CaOH^+(aq) \qquad \textbf{5-69}$$

$$K_4{}^0 = \frac{(a_{CaOH^+})}{(a_{Ca^{2+}})(a_{OH^-})} = 25 \qquad \textbf{5-70}$$

$$H_2O(l) \rightleftharpoons H^+(aq) + OH^-(aq) \qquad \textbf{5-71}$$

The above equilibrium constants are for a temperature of 25°C.

The question arises as to which of these equilibria are of importance in determining the solubility of calcium fluoride in a solution of given *pH*. To arrive at an answer, we must write equations for the mass balances of fluoride and calcium ions and determine the concentrations of the various species at each *pH*. For calcium, the molar solubility S is equal to total calcium concentration C_{Ca}.

$$S = C_{Ca} = [Ca^{2+}] + [CaOH^+] + [CaF^+] \qquad \textbf{5-72}$$

and for fluoride, the total concentration is C_F.

$$C_F = [F^-] + [CaF^+] + [HF] + 2[HF_2^-] = 2S \qquad \textbf{5-73}$$

As a first approximation, let us assume that $[CaOH^+]$, $[CaF^+]$, and $[HF_2^-]$ are small and negligible compared to the concentrations of other species present. We may assume this because of the relative numerical values of the equilibrium constants. Then we may write

$$S = C_{Ca} \cong [Ca^{2+}] \qquad \textbf{5-74}$$

and

$$2S = C_F = [F^-] + [HF] \qquad \textbf{5-75}$$

The concentrations of calcium ion and fluoride ion are related through the solubility product constant expression

$$K_s^0 = [Ca^{2+}][F^-]^2 y_2 y_1^2 \qquad \textbf{5-76}$$

where y_2 is the activity coefficient of calcium ion and y_1 is that for fluoride ion or other singly charged ions.

We can calculate the values of the activity coefficients from Eq. 5-28. For calcium ion and other doubly charged ions, $y_2 = 0.356$, and for singly charged ions, $y_1 = 0.773$ at $I = 0.1$.

Before these equations may be solved simultaneously, we must eliminate the concentration of undissociated hydrogen fluoride. This can be done through the equilibrium condition, for Eq. 5-63, which expresses the concentration of hydrogen fluoride in terms of hydrogen ion and fluoride ion concentrations

$$[HF] = \frac{[H^+][F^-]y_1^2}{K_a^0} \qquad \textbf{5-77}$$

Substituting in Eq. 5-75, we obtain

$$2S = [F^-] + \frac{[H^+][F^-]y_1^2}{K_a^0} \qquad \textbf{5-78}$$

$$2S = [F^-]\left(1 + \frac{[H^+]y_1^2}{K_a^0}\right) \qquad \textbf{5-79}$$

Solving Eqs. 5-76 and 5-81 for $[Ca^{2+}]$ and $[F^-]$ respectively, and substituting in Eq. 5-78, we can obtain the relationship

$$S^3 = \frac{K_s^0\left(1 + \frac{[H^+]y_1^2}{K_a^0}\right)^2}{4y_2y_1^2} \qquad \textbf{5-80} \qquad\qquad S = \sqrt[3]{\frac{K_s^0\left(1 + \frac{[H^+]y_1^2}{K_a^0}\right)^2}{4y_2y_1^2}} \qquad \textbf{5-81}$$

This equation gives the solubility of calcium fluoride as a function of hydrogen ion concentration, assuming equilibria represented by Eqs. 5-65, 5-67 and 5-69 are of no consequence; this assumption will be subjected to test.

Let us calculate the solubility of calcium fluoride in aqueous buffer solutions at various *pH* values assuming the ionic strength I to be constant at 0.10. It must further be assumed that the ions and molecules of the buffer, other than hydrogen and hydroxide ions, do not react with calcium or fluoride ions; the ions of the buffer, however, do contribute to the ionic strength of the solution.

At $pH = 2$, $[H^+] = 1 \times 10^{-2}$ M, and S is calculated from Eq. 5-81 to be 1.57×10^{-3} M

$$S = [Ca^{2+}] = 1.57 \times 10^{-3} \, M$$

From Eq. 5-76

$$[F^-] = \sqrt{\frac{K_s^0}{[Ca^{2+}]y_2 y_1^2}} = \sqrt{\frac{3.4 \times 10^{-11}}{(1.57 \times 10^{-3})(0.356)(0.773)^2}} \quad \textbf{5-82}$$

$$[F^-] = 3.19 \times 10^{-4} \, M$$

From Eq. 5-77

$$[HF] = \frac{[H^+][F^-]y_1^2}{K_a^0}$$

$$[HF] = 2.82 \times 10^{-3} \, M$$

Let us use the equilibrium conditions for Eqs. 5-65, 5-67, and 5-69 to determine what concentrations of CaF^+, $CaOH^+$, and HF_2^- could exist in an aqueous solution with $[F^-] = 3.19 \times 10^{-4}$ M, $pH = 2$, and $I = 0.1$. These calculated concentrations will be very close to the equilibrium values.

From Eq. 5-66

$$[HF_2^-] = K_2^0 [HF][F^-] \quad \textbf{5-83}$$

$$[HF_2^-] = 3.51 \times 10^{-6} \, M$$

From Eq. 5-68

$$[CaF^+] = K_3^0 [Ca^{2+}][F^-]y_2 \quad \textbf{5-84}$$

$$[CaF^+] \leq 1.78 \times 10^{-6} \, M$$

From Eq. 5-70

$$[CaOH^+] = K_4^0 [Ca^{2+}][OH^-]y_2 \quad \textbf{5-85}$$

$$[CaOH^+] = 1.40 \times 10^{-14} \, M$$

Returning now to the mass balance equations, we find

$$S = C_{Ca} = 1.57 \times 10^{-3} + 1.40 \times 10^{-14} + 1.78 \times 10^{-6} \cong 1.57 \times 10^{-3}\ M$$
$$2S = C_F = 3.19 \times 10^{-4} + 1.78 \times 10^{-6} + 2.82 \times 10^{-3} + 3.51 \times 10^{-6}$$
$$\cong 3.14 \times 10^{-3}$$
$$S = \frac{3.14}{2} \times 10^{-3} = 1.57 \times 10^{-3}\ M$$

Thus we see that the mass balances for both calcium and fluoride ions yield the same value of S. Note that the contributions of the species CaF^+, $CaOH^+$, and HF_2^- to the total solubility are negligible.

The solubility of CaF_2 was calculated using Eq. 5-81. Figure 5-4 shows the plot of log S *vs. pH* which was obtained. As *pH* increases from 1 to 4, the solubility of CaF_2 decreases markedly. When the majority of the fluoride is present in solution as fluoride ion, the solubility is no longer *pH* dependent and levels off to a constant value. If the solution were to be made basic enough so that the concentration of the species $CaOH^+$ were to become important, the solubility of calcium fluoride would again increase.

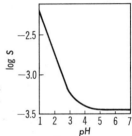

Figure 5-4 Solubility of calcium fluoride as a function of *pH*. Ionic strength is 0.10; temperature 25°C.

Problems

5-1 (a) From the data in Table 5-2 calculate the solubility of barium sulfate in water at 298°K assuming that neither barium nor sulfate ions hydrolyze.
(b) Determine the solubility of $BaSO_4$ in a 0.10 M solution of NaCl.
(c) Determine the solubility in a 0.020 M NaHSO₄ solution.
(d) Determine the solubility in a 0.020 M BaCl₂ solution.

5-2 The following data were supplied by Mr. K. Jeffrey Johnson from an undergraduate research project which he performed at the College of St. Thomas, 1965. From the solubilities of $SrSO_4$ in LiClO₄ solutions of various concentrations, determine K_s and K_s^0 for SrSO₄. Calculate activity coefficients from Eq. 5-27.

[LiClO₄]	[SrSO₄]
0.0026 M	$6.4 \times 10^{-4}\ M$
0.0104	8.0×10^{-4}
0.0180	9.1×10^{-4}
0.0254	9.6×10^{-4}
0.0404	1.14×10^{-3}

5-3   The solubility product, $K_s{}^0$, for thallous thiocyanate is 1.4×10^{-4} at $298°K$. Assuming activities are equal to concentrations, and that no other reactions occur involving thallous and thiocyanate ions, make a plot of $[Tl^+]$ *vs.* $[SCN^-]$ and a plot of $[Tl^+]$ *vs.* $1/[SCN^-]$. Can complete precipitation ever be achieved? Explain your answer.

5-4   Consider the following equilibria and the appropriate constants at $298°K$.

$$AgSCN(s) \rightleftharpoons Ag^+(aq) + SCN^-(aq) \qquad\qquad K_s{}^0 = 1.6 \times 10^{-12}$$

$$Ag^+(aq) + 2SCN^-(aq) \rightleftharpoons Ag(SCN)_2{}^-(aq) \qquad \beta_2{}^0 = 1.5 \times 10^8$$

$$Ag^+(aq) + 3SCN^-(aq) \rightleftharpoons Ag(SCN)_3{}^{2-}(aq) \qquad \beta_3{}^0 = 2.0 \times 10^{10}$$

$$Ag^+(aq) + 4SCN^-(aq) \rightleftharpoons Ag(SCN)_4{}^{3-}(aq) \qquad \beta_4{}^0 = 1.0 \times 10^{11}$$

Assuming activities are equal to concentrations,
   (a) Calculate S as a function of the equilibrium concentration of thiocyanate ion.
   (b) What is the concentration of each metal complex ion when the equilibrium concentration of thiocyanate ion is $1.0\ M$?
   (c) What is the total analytical concentration of thiocyanate ion when the equilibrium concentration of thiocyanate ion is $1.0\ M$?

5-5   The following data were obtained by J. H. Jonte and D. S. Martin [*J. Am. Chem. Soc.*, **74**, 2052 (1952)] from a study of the solubility of silver chloride in solutions prepared by mixing a solution of silver perchlorate and perchloric acid with a sodium chloride solution. When equilibrium was established at 15°C, the following data were obtained for the concentration of silver ion and chloride ion in the saturated solutions of the ionic strength indicated.

$[Cl^-]$	$[Ag^+]$	$I^{1/2}$
$5.48 \times 10^{-5}\ M$	$1.77 \times 10^{-6}\ M$	0.161
1.11×10^{-4}	8.91×10^{-7}	.094
2.01×10^{-4}	5.75×10^{-7}	.174
3.74×10^{-4}	3.89×10^{-7}	.149
5.50×10^{-4}	2.69×10^{-7}	.092
9.65×10^{-4}	2.75×10^{-7}	.123
1.10×10^{-3}	2.75×10^{-7}	.094
1.26×10^{-3}	2.46×10^{-7}	.122
1.59×10^{-3}	2.46×10^{-7}	.091
2.75×10^{-3}	2.40×10^{-7}	.094
5.50×10^{-3}	2.57×10^{-7}	.111
1.10×10^{-2}	2.82×10^{-7}	.141
2.75×10^{-2}	6.46×10^{-7}	.165
5.50×10^{-2}	9.12×10^{-7}	.248
1.10×10^{-1}	2.04×10^{-6}	.345

Using activity coefficients calculated from Eq. 5-27, determine $K_s{}^0$, $\beta_1{}^0$, and $\beta_2{}^0$. Hint: $K_s{}^0$ and $\beta_1{}^0$ may be determined in a manner similar to an example in this chapter. The student should use his ingenuity to determine $\beta_2{}^0$.

CHAPTER **6**

Oxidation-Reduction

In Chapter 4 we discussed acid-base equilibria and complex equilibria and in Chapter 5 we considered heterogeneous equilibria. None of these equilibria involve a change in oxidation number of any element in the reactions. Reactions which involve changes in oxidation numbers of elements are known as *oxidation-reduction* reactions. Oxidation is defined as a process in which electrons are apparently lost and conversely reduction is defined as a process in which electrons are apparently gained. In order to have a complete reaction one substance must be undergoing oxidation while a second substance undergoes reduction.

6–A   THE NERNST EQUATION

Iron in the oxidation state $+2$ can lose an electron and is oxidized to the $+3$ state as shown by the equation

$$Fe^{2+}(aq) \rightleftharpoons Fe^{3+}(aq) + e^- \qquad \text{6-1}$$

Cerium in the oxidation state $+4$ gains an electron in being reduced to oxidation state $+3$ as shown by the equation

$$Ce^{4+}(aq) + e^- \rightleftharpoons Ce^{3+}(aq) \qquad \text{6-2}$$

The total reaction between Fe^{2+} and Ce^{4+} when their solutions are mixed, may be written

$$Ce^{4+}(aq) + Fe^{2+}(aq) \rightleftharpoons Ce^{3+}(aq) + Fe^{3+}(aq) \qquad \text{6-3}$$

The free energy change for this reaction is

$$\Delta G = \mu_{Ce^{3+}} + \mu_{Fe^{3+}} - \mu_{Ce^{4+}} - \mu_{Fe^{2+}} \qquad \text{6-4}$$

Using Eq. 3-7 to define chemical potentials and Eq. 4-10 to define activities, ΔG becomes

$$\Delta G = [\mu^0{}_{Ce^{3+}} + RT \ln a_{Ce^{3+}}] + [\mu^0{}_{Fe^{3+}} + RT \ln a_{Fe^{3+}}$$
$$- [\mu^0{}_{Fe^{2+}} + RT \ln a_{Fe^{2+}}] - [\mu^0{}_{Ce^{4+}} + RT \ln a_{Ce^{4+}}] \qquad \textbf{6-5}$$

On collecting terms, we obtain

$$\Delta G = \mu^0{}_{Fe^{3+}} + \mu^0{}_{Ce^{3+}} - \mu^0{}_{Ce^{4+}} - \mu^0{}_{Fe^{2+}} + RT \ln \frac{a_{Fe^{3+}} a_{Ce^{3+}}}{a_{Fe^{2+}} a_{Ce^{4+}}} \qquad \textbf{6-6}$$

Since

$$\Delta G^0 = \mu^0{}_{Fe^{3+}} + \mu^0{}_{Ce^{3+}} - \mu^0{}_{Fe^{2+}} - \mu^0{}_{Ce^{4+}} \qquad \textbf{6-7}$$

$$\Delta G = \Delta G^0 + RT \ln \frac{a_{Fe^{3+}} a_{Ce^{3+}}}{a_{Fe^{2+}} a_{Ce^{4+}}} = \Delta G^0 + RT \ln Q^0 \qquad \textbf{6-8}$$

As with other types of reactions, ΔG^0 is related to K^0 by the equation

$$\Delta G^0 = -RT \ln K^0 \qquad \textbf{6-9}$$

A galvanic cell is formed by a combination of two electrodes such that oxidation takes place at one electrode and reduction takes place at the other. We can arrange the component parts of the reaction shown by Eq. 6-3 so that the half-reaction shown by Eq. 6-1 takes place at the left electrode of a galvanic cell, and the half-reaction shown by Eq. 6-2 takes place at the right electrode of a galvanic cell. Equation 6-3 would then represent the reaction for the cell

$$Pt|Fe^{2+}, Fe^{3+}|\ |Ce^{4+}, Ce^{3+}|Pt \qquad \textbf{6-10}$$

The electromotive force, e.m.f., of such a galvanic cell is directly related to the free energy change of the reaction occurring.

We have previously defined the free energy change, ΔG, as the maximum possible useful work a system can do when a chemical reaction occurs. When the reaction is allowed to occur in a galvanic cell under conditions where the maximum possible electrical work is done, the definitions may be stated as

$$\Delta G = -n \mathscr{F} \Delta \mathscr{E} \qquad \textbf{6-11}$$

$$\Delta G^0 = -n \mathscr{F} \Delta \mathscr{E}^0 \qquad \textbf{6-12}$$

where n is the number of equivalents of electrons transferred in the chemical reaction, $\mathscr{F}$ is the value of the Faraday, 23,060 cal/(volt-equivalent). $\Delta \mathscr{E}^0$ is the e.m.f. in volts that will be measured for a cell reaction if all reactants and products are at unit activity and $\Delta \mathscr{E}$ is the e.m.f. in volts that will be measured when the activities of reactants and products are different from unity.

On combination of Eqs. 6-11 and 6-12 with 6-8, the result is

$$\Delta \mathscr{E} = \Delta \mathscr{E}^0 - \frac{RT}{n \mathscr{F}} \ln \frac{a_{Fe^{3+}} a_{Ce^{3+}}}{a_{Fe^{2+}} a_{Ce^{4+}}} \qquad \textbf{6-13}$$

This equation is in the form of the Nernst Equation which shows the relationship between $\Delta\mathscr{E}$, $\Delta\mathscr{E}^0$ and the activities of the chemical species in the system. For the generalized oxidation reduction reaction the Nernst Equation takes the form

$$A_{(reduced)} + B_{(oxidized)} \rightleftharpoons A_{(oxidized)} + B_{(reduced)}$$

$$\Delta\mathscr{E} = \Delta\mathscr{E}^0 - \frac{RT}{n\mathscr{F}} \ln \frac{a_{A(oxidized)}a_{B(reduced)}}{a_{A(reduced)}a_{B(oxidized)}} \qquad \text{6-14}$$

or

$$\Delta\mathscr{E} = \Delta\mathscr{E}^0 - \frac{RT}{n\mathscr{F}} \ln Q^0 \qquad \text{6-15}$$

6–B   STANDARD OXIDATION POTENTIALS

The oxidation potential of a substance is a measure of the ease (or difficulty) with which the substance can be oxidized. However, while we often speak of the standard oxidation potential for a half-reaction, it is not possible to measure it. Likewise it is not possible to measure the absolute value of the potential of the corresponding single electrode or half-cell. It is possible to determine only the difference in potential or e.m.f. between two electrodes of a complete cell. For example, the e.m.f. of the cell shown below has been determined to be -0.770 volts.

$$Pt|Fe^{2+}(aq., a = 1), Fe^{3+}(aq., a = 1)| \, |H^+(aq., a = 1)|H_2(g, 1 \text{ atm})|Pt \qquad \text{6-16}$$

Since all reactants and products are at unit activity the e.m.f. of the cell is -0.77 volts and corresponds to the $\Delta\mathscr{E}^0$. We can define the potential of the standard hydrogen electrode by the symbol $\mathscr{E}^0_{(H_2, H^+)}$ and the potential of the standard ferrous-ferric electrode by the symbol $\mathscr{E}^0_{(Fe^{2+}, Fe^{3+})}$. We can write

$$\Delta\mathscr{E}^0 = \mathscr{E}^0_{(Fe^{2+}, Fe^{3+})} - \mathscr{E}^0_{(H_2, H^+)} = -0.77 \text{ V} \qquad \text{6-17}$$

To get a working system of oxidation potentials, we can arbitrarily assign a value to some one electrode and measure all other electrodes relative to it. By almost universal agreement among scientists, the reference electrode chosen is the standard hydrogen electrode which has been assigned the value of zero volts, *i.e.*, $\mathscr{E}^0_{(H_2, H^+)} = 0$. Therefore, we can substitute this value in Eq. 6-16 to obtain

$$\mathscr{E}^0_{(Fe^{2+}, Fe^{3+})} = -0.77 - \mathscr{E}^0_{(H_2, H^+)} = -0.77 \text{ V}$$

In general, the *oxidation potential* for any single half-reaction is defined as the e.m.f. of a *cell* in which one electrode is the standard hydrogen electrode and the second electrode is one involving the components of the half-reaction in question. For the cell

$$Pt|Fe^{2+}(aq., a \neq 1),\ Fe^{3+}(aq., a \neq 1)\|H^+(aq., a = 1)|H_2(g,\ 1\ atm),\ Pt \qquad 6\text{-}18$$

in which the activities of the species present in the left half-cell are different from unity, an equation similar to Eq. 6-13 can be derived for the e.m.f.

$$\Delta\mathscr{E} = \Delta\mathscr{E}^0 - \frac{RT}{n\mathscr{F}} \ln \frac{a_{Fe^{3+}}(p_{H^{2+}})^{1/2}}{a_{Fe^{2+}}a_{H^+}} \qquad 6\text{-}19$$

$\Delta\mathscr{E}$ represents the potential difference between the $Fe^{2+} - Fe^{3+}$ electrode and the standard hydrogen electrode

$$\Delta\mathscr{E} = \mathscr{E}_{(Fe^{2+},\ Fe^{3+})} - \mathscr{E}^0_{(H_2,\ H^+)} \qquad 6\text{-}20$$

Substitution of Eqs. 6-17 and 6-20 into Eq. 6-19 yields the result

$$\mathscr{E}_{(Fe^{2+},\ Fe^{3+})} - \mathscr{E}^0_{(H_2,\ H^+)} = \mathscr{E}^0_{(Fe^{2+},\ Fe^{3+})} - \mathscr{E}^0_{(H_2,\ H^+)}$$
$$- \frac{RT}{n\mathscr{F}} \ln \frac{a_{Fe^{3+}}(p_{H_2})^{1/2}}{a_{Fe^{2+}}a_{H^+}} \qquad 6\text{-}21$$

Since $a_{H^+} = 1$ and $p_{H_2} = 1$ in a standard hydrogen electrode, we obtain the result

$$\mathscr{E}_{(Fe^{2+},\ Fe^{3+})} = \mathscr{E}^0_{(Fe^{2+},\ Fe^{3+})} - \frac{RT}{n\mathscr{F}} \ln \frac{a_{Fe^{3+}}}{a_{Fe^{2+}}} \qquad 6\text{-}22$$

The value of $\mathscr{E}_{(Fe^{2+},\ Fe^{3+})}$ given by Eq. 6-22 corresponds to the e.m.f. for the cell reaction

$$Fe^{2+}(aq., a \neq 1) + H^+(aq., a = 1) \rightleftharpoons$$
$$Fe^{3+}(aq., a \neq 1) + 1/2\,H_2(g,\ 1\ atm) \qquad 6\text{-}23$$

From the definition presented earlier in this section, the value of $\mathscr{E}_{(Fe^{2+}, Fe^{3+})}$ corresponds also to the oxidation potential of the ferrous-ferric half-reaction at specified activities. Consider the general case of the half-cell whose reaction is

$$A_{(reduced)} \rightleftharpoons A_{(oxidized)} + ne^-$$

When coupled with a standard hydrogen electrode, the measured e.m.f. of the cell is the oxidation potential of the couple and is given by the equation

$$\mathscr{E} = \mathscr{E}^0 - \frac{RT}{n\mathscr{F}} \ln \frac{a_{A(oxidized)}}{a_{A(reduced)}} \qquad 6\text{-}24$$

This equation is also a form of the Nernst Equation. When the activity of the reduced and oxidized forms are both unity and also when their ratio is unity, the oxidation potential is equal to the standard oxidation potentials, *i.e.*, $\mathscr{E} = \mathscr{E}^0$.

Figure 6-1 shows a schematic representation of the oxidation potential of *three couples*. We have stated that the value of $\Delta\mathscr{E}^0$

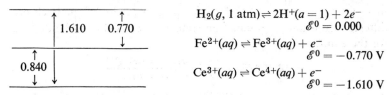

$$H_2(g, 1\ atm) \rightleftharpoons 2H^+(a = 1) + 2e^-$$
$$\mathscr{E}^0 = 0.000$$
$$Fe^{2+}(aq) \rightleftharpoons Fe^{3+}(aq) + e^-$$
$$\mathscr{E}^0 = -0.770\ V$$
$$Ce^{3+}(aq) \rightleftharpoons Ce^{4+}(aq) + e^-$$
$$\mathscr{E}^0 = -1.610\ V$$

Figure 6-1 Relative oxidation potentials.

for the cell in 6-14 is -0.770 volts and that this is the oxidation potential for the half-reaction

$$Fe^{2+}(aq., a = 1) \rightleftharpoons Fe^{3+}(aq., a = 1) + e^-$$

For similar half-cell involving $Ce^{3+}(aq)$ and $Ce^{4+}(aq)$ measured against a standard hydrogen electrode, we find $\Delta\mathscr{E}^0 = -1.610$ volts and hence the oxidation potential for the half-reaction is -1.610 volts

$$Ce^{3+}(aq., a = 1) \rightleftharpoons Ce^{4+}(aq., a = 1) + e^-$$

These values demonstrate that under conditions of unit activity, $Ce^{3+}(aq)$ is oxidized less readily than either $Fe^{2+}(aq)$ or $H_2(g)$.

Appendix IV contains a number of half-reactions and their oxidation potentials. The reader is referred to Appendix VI for references to extensive tabulations of half-reactions and oxidation potentials.

In the types of electrodes employing half-reactions such as those shown by Eq. 6-1 or 6-2, two oxidation states of the element involved are in contact with an inert electrode. In addition, there are two other electrode types commonly encountered. One electrode is a metal or nonmetal in contact with a solution of its ion. An example of such an electrode is

$$Cu(s)|Cu^{2+}(aq) \qquad \textbf{6-25}$$

where the half-reaction occurring can be written

$$Cu(s) \rightleftharpoons Cu^{2+}(aq) + 2e^- \qquad \textbf{6-26}$$

The other type is a metal electrode in contact with an insoluble salt and the anion of the insoluble metal salt. An example of such an electrode is

$$Ag(s), AgCl(s)|Cl^-(aq) \qquad \textbf{6-27}$$

where the reaction occurring can be written

$$Ag(s) + Cl^-(aq) \rightleftharpoons AgCl(s) + e^- \qquad \textbf{6-28}$$

6–C   EQUILIBRIUM CONSTANTS FOR OXIDATION-REDUCTION REACTIONS FROM STANDARD OXIDATION POTENTIALS

To determine the extent to which a particular oxidation-reduction reaction will occur when equilibrium is established, the numerical value of the equilibrium constant must be known. This can be obtained provided the value of $\Delta \mathscr{E}^0$ is known. When the reactants and products have reached equilibrium, ΔG for the reaction has become zero, and therefore from Eq. 6-11, $\Delta \mathscr{E}$ must be zero. Further, at equilibrium, the term Q^0 is numerically equal to K^0 and therefore Eq. 6-15 becomes

$$0 = \Delta \mathscr{E}^0 - \frac{RT}{n\mathscr{F}} \ln K^0 \qquad \text{6-29}$$

On substitution of numerical values for R, T, and $\mathscr{F}$, Eq. 6-29 at 25°C becomes

$$\Delta \mathscr{E}^0 = \frac{.059}{n} \log K^0 \qquad \text{6-30}$$

To obtain a complete oxidation-reduction reaction from two half-reactions, one multiplies each half-reaction by a factor such that the number of electrons in the two half-reactions is the same; one half-reaction is then substracted from the second to obtain the desired net oxidation-reduction equation. To obtain a value of $\Delta \mathscr{E}^0$, the $\mathscr{E}^0$ value for the first half-reaction is substracted algebraically from the second.

Strictly speaking, the standard free energy change for the overall reaction should first be evaluated and the value of K^0 should then be calculated from Equation 6-9. ΔG^0 for the reaction is the algebraic difference in the standard free energy changes associated with the oxidation potentials of the two half-reactions in question. The value of ΔG^0 for each half-reaction is $-n\mathscr{F}\mathscr{E}^0$. The procedure outlined, using $\Delta \mathscr{E}^0$ to evaluate $\log K^0$ is, when carried out correctly, equivalent to using ΔG^0.

Suppose a question to be answered is the following: "What fraction of a 0.1 M $Fe^{3+}(aq)$ solution is not reduced by a 0.05 M $H_2SO_3(aq)$ solution when the concentration of hydrogen ion is 1.0 mole/liter?" When H_2SO_3 behaves as a reducing agent, it is oxidized to $SO_4^{2-}(aq)$ and when $Fe^{3+}(aq)$ is reduced by $H_2SO_3(aq)$ it forms $Fe^{2+}(aq)$. From Appendix IV, find the appropriate half-reactions and their $\mathscr{E}^0$ values.

(A) $H_2SO_3(aq) + H_2O(l) \rightleftharpoons SO_4^{2-}(aq) + 4\,H^+(aq) + 2e^-$
$$\mathscr{E}_A^0 = -0.20 \text{ V} \qquad \text{6-31}$$

(B) $Fe^{2+}(aq) \rightleftharpoons Fe^{3+}(aq) + e^-$ $\qquad \mathscr{E}_B^0 = -0.77 \text{ V} \qquad$ 6-32

Since two electrons are lost by $H_2SO_3(aq)$ and only one gained by

104

$Fe^{2+}(aq)$, we must multiply the second by 2.

$$(B')\ \ 2\,Fe^{2+}(aq) \rightleftharpoons 2\,Fe^{3+}(aq) + e^{-*} \qquad \mathscr{E}_{B'}{}^0 = -0.77\ V \qquad \textbf{6-33}$$

Subtracting the iron half-reaction from the H_2SO_3 half-reaction, we obtain for the desired reaction the equation

$$2\,Fe^{3+}(aq) + H_2SO_3(aq) + H_2O(l) \rightleftharpoons 2\,Fe^{2+}(aq) + SO_4{}^{2-}(aq) + 4\,H^+(aq)$$

$$\textbf{6-34}$$

$\Delta\mathscr{E}^0$ is given by the equation

$$\Delta\mathscr{E}^0 = \mathscr{E}_A{}^0 - \mathscr{E}_{B'}{}^0 = -0.20 - (-.77) = +.57\ V \qquad \textbf{6-35}$$

for which the value of n is 2. On substitution in Eq. 6-30, we obtain

$$+0.57 = \frac{.059}{2}\log K^0 \qquad \textbf{6-36}$$

Solving, we obtain the result $K^0 = 2 \times 10^{19}$.

Returning now to the fraction of $Fe^{3+}(aq)$ not reduced by the H_2SO_3. The total iron concentration is given by the equation

$$[Fe^{2+}] + [Fe^{3+}] = 0.1 \qquad \textbf{6-37}$$

At equilibrium, $[Fe^{3+}] = 2\ [H_2SO_3]$ and $[Fe^{2+}] = 2\ [SO_4{}^{2-}]$ and therefore

$$\frac{[Fe^{2+}]}{[Fe^{3+}]} = \frac{[SO_4{}^{2-}]}{[H_2SO_3]} \qquad \textbf{6-38}$$

The equilibrium constant for the reaction shown by Eq. 6-34 is given by

$$K^0 = \frac{[Fe^{2+}]^2[SO_4{}^{2-}][H^+]^4}{[Fe^{3+}]^2[H_2SO_3]} \qquad \textbf{6-39}$$

Substituting for $[SO_4{}^{2-}]/[H_2SO_3]$ from Eq. 6-38, and remembering that $[H^+] = 1.0$ mole/liter, we obtain the result that

$$K^0 = \frac{[Fe^{2+}]^3}{[Fe^{3+}]^3} \qquad \textbf{6-40}$$

or that

$$\frac{[Fe^{2+}]}{[Fe^{3+}]} = \sqrt[3]{K^0} = 2.7 \times 10^6 \qquad \textbf{6-41}$$

Let the fraction of iron remaining as Fe^{3+} be X

$$X = \frac{[Fe^{3+}]}{[Fe^{2+}] + [Fe^{3+}]} = \frac{[Fe^{2+}]/2.7 \times 10^6}{[Fe^{2+}] + [Fe^{2+}]/2.7 \times 10^6} = \frac{1}{2.7 \times 10^6} \qquad \textbf{6-42}$$

$$X = 3.7 \times 10^{-7} \text{ or } 3.7 \times 10^{-5}\%$$

Thus the great majority of Fe^{3+} is reduced.

---

* Note that while the ferrous-ferric half-reaction was multiplied by 2, the value of $\mathscr{E}_B{}^0$ does not change.

6–D   DETERMINATION OF SOLUBILITY PRODUCTS

Just as equilibrium constants for oxidation-reduction reactions can be obtained from oxidation potentials, it is also sometimes possible to obtain equilibrium constants for nonoxidation-reduction reactions. For the solubility equilibrium of solid silver chloride in water we write

$$AgCl(s) \rightleftharpoons Ag^+(aq) + Cl^-(aq) \qquad \textbf{6-43}$$

for which the solubility product constant is

$$K_s^0 = a_{Ag^+}a_{Cl^-} \qquad \textbf{6-44}$$

To calculate K_s^0, one must determine the activity of silver ion and the activity of chloride ion in a saturated solution of silver choride. It is fortunate that both activities can be determined in galvanic cells.

The electromotive force measured for the galvanic cell

$$Ag(s)|Ag^+(a = 1)|\,|H^+(a = 1)|H_2(g, 1 \text{ atm}), Pt \qquad \textbf{6-45}$$

is -0.799 volts, so the standard oxidation potential is that for the reaction

$$Ag(s) \rightleftharpoons Ag^+(aq) + e^- \qquad \textbf{6-46}$$

The Nernst Equation relates the activity of silver ion to the oxidation potential for the silver-silver ion half-reaction

$$\mathscr{E}_{Ag, Ag^+} = \mathscr{E}^0_{Ag, Ag^+} - 0.059 \log(a_{Ag^+}) \qquad \textbf{6-47}$$

The e.m.f. measured for the cell

$$Ag(s), AgCl(s)|Cl^-(aq., a = 1)\,|\,|H^+(aq., a = 1)|H_2(g.1\text{atm}), Pt \qquad \textbf{6-48}$$

is -0.222 volts, and so the standard oxidation potential is -0.222 volts for the half-reaction shown by the equation

$$Ag(s) + Cl^-(aq) \rightleftharpoons AgCl(s) + e^- \qquad \textbf{6-49}$$

The Nernst Equation relates the activity of chloride ion to the oxidation potential for the silver-silver chloride half-reaction

$$\mathscr{E}_{Ag, AgCl, Cl^-} = \mathscr{E}^0_{Ag, AgCl, Cl^-} + .0591 \log(a_{Cl^-}) \qquad \textbf{6-50}$$

The potential of the silver electrode in the cell represented by Eq. 6-48 must be given by both Eqs. 6-47 and 6-50 because the silver metal in the half-cell must be in equilibrium with *both* $Ag^+(aq)$ and $Cl^-(aq)$ when solid AgCl is present. This means here $\mathscr{E}_{Ag, Ag^+} = \mathscr{E}_{Ag, AgCl, Cl^-}$. Taking the logarithm of both sides of Eq. 6-44, we obtain the equation

$$\log K_s^0 = \log(a_{Ag^+}) + \log(a_{Cl^-}) \qquad \textbf{6-51}$$

Substituting from Eqs. 6-47 and 6-50, Eq. 6-51 becomes

$$\log K_s^0 = \frac{\mathscr{E}^0{}_{Ag, Ag^+} - \mathscr{E}_{Ag, Ag^+}}{.059} + \frac{\mathscr{E}_{Ag, AgCl, Cl^-} - \mathscr{E}^0{}_{Ag, AgCl, Cl^-}}{.059}$$

6-52

Since $\mathscr{E}_{Ag, Ag^+} = \mathscr{E}_{Ag, AgCl, Cl^-}$, we obtain

$$\log K_s^0 = \frac{\mathscr{E}^0{}_{Ag, Ag^+} - \mathscr{E}^0{}_{Ag, AgCl, Cl^-}}{.059}$$

6-53

Putting in the numerical values cited earlier for the standard potentials

$$\log K_s^0 = \frac{-.799 + .222}{.059} = \frac{-.577}{.059} = -9.76$$

$$K_s^0 = 1.7 \times 10^{-10}$$

This value of K_s^0 is accepted as the solubility product of silver chloride. The measurement of potentials for such pairs of cells is a method for determination of solubility products. Once the necessary $\mathscr{E}^0$ values are known, K_s^0 may also be calculated as above, or in a manner similar to that shown in the preceding section for equilibrium constants of oxidation-reduction reactions.

6–E   DETERMINATION OF COMPLEX ION FORMATION CONSTANTS FROM E. M. F. MEASUREMENTS

This method is based on a measurement of activity of a solvated metal ion when the ion is in equilibrium with the various complex species in the system. The standard oxidation potential corresponding to the half-reaction

$$M(s) \rightleftharpoons M^+(aq) + e^-$$

6-54

is governed by the Nernst Equation

$$\mathscr{E} = \mathscr{E}^0 - \frac{RT}{n\mathscr{F}} \ln a_{M^+}$$

6-55

As M^+ becomes complexed by ligand X^-

$$M^+(aq) + jX^-(aq) \rightleftharpoons MX_j^{(+1-j)}$$

6-56

the activity of the metal ion is reduced and the oxidation potential increases as required by Eq. 6-55.

We shall analyze the data for a specific case to see how equilibrium constants can be determined through potentiometric methods. Consider the formation of thiocyanate complexes of cadmium ion having various ligand to metal ratios as shown by the general equation

$$Cd^{2+}(aq) + jSCN^-(aq) \rightleftharpoons Cd(SCN)_j^{(2-j)}$$

6-57

$$\beta_j = \frac{[Cd(SCN)_j^{(2-j)}]}{[Cd^{2+}][SCN^-]^j}$$

6-58

Experimentally, the e.m.f. of the cell

$$Cd|Cd(ClO_4)_2(1 \times 10^{-4}M), NaClO_4(2M-XM), NaSCN(XM)||NaClO_4(2M),$$
$$Cd(ClO_4)_2(1 \times 10^{-4} M)|Cd \qquad \text{6-59}$$

is determined as a function of sodium thiocyanate concentration. Data for such a system are presented in Table 6-1. When no sodium thiocyanate is present in the solution, the e.m.f. of the cell is zero because both half-cells are identical. When the concentration of thiocyanate increases, the e.m.f. increases. Since the total ionic strength is constant for the above cell, the activity coefficients of the ions should be constant. Because the ionic strength of the solution is high, only concentration constants will be calculated. It will be assumed that concentrations can replace activities in the Nernst Equation.

Table VI-1

Variation of $\Delta\mathscr{E}$ and $F_j(X)$ as a Function of [NaSCN] at 25°C and $I = 1.0$

[NaSCN]	$\Delta\mathscr{E}$	$F_0(X)$	$F_1(X)$	$F_2(X)$
0.000 M	0.0000 V			
0.100	0.0126	2.67	16.7	67
0.200	0.0244	5.71	23.6	68
0.300	0.0295	9.96	29.9	66
0.400	0.0353	15.6	36.5	66

To evaluate equilibrium constants from this data, we must first write an equation for the e.m.f. of the cell

$$\Delta\mathscr{E} = \mathscr{E}_L - \mathscr{E}_R = \left(\mathscr{E}^0{}_{Cd^{2+}} - \frac{RT}{n\mathscr{F}}\ln[Cd^{2+}]_L\right) - \left(\mathscr{E}^0{}_{Cd^{2+}} - \frac{RT}{2\mathscr{F}}\ln[Cd^{2+}]_R\right)$$
$$\text{6-60}$$

where the subscripts L and R signify the left hand and right hand half-cell respectively. Since no complexing agent is added to the right hand half-cell, $[Cd^{2+}]_R = 1 \times 10^{-4} M$, but since thiocyanate ion is added to the left hand half-cell the concentration of cadmium ion at equilibrium will be less than $1 \times 10^{-4} M$. Eq. 6-38 reduces to

$$\Delta\mathscr{E} = -\frac{RT}{2\mathscr{F}}\ln[Cd^{2+}]_L + \frac{RT}{2\mathscr{F}}\ln(1 \times 10^{-4}) \qquad \text{6-61}$$

We must next write mass balances for cadmium ion and for thiocyanate ion in the left hand half-cell

$$C_{Cd} = [Cd^{2+}] + [CdSCN^+] + [Cd(SCN)_2] + \cdots \qquad \textbf{6-62}$$

$$C_{SCN^-} = [SCN^-] + [CdSCN^+] + 2[Cd(SCN)_2] + \cdots \qquad \textbf{6-63}$$

Since the concentration of sodium thiocyanate is so much larger than the total cadmium ion concentration, the amount of thiocyanate "lost" by being bound in the complex may be considered negligible, so that

$$C_{SCN^-} \cong [SCN^-]$$

The total cadmium ion concentration in the left-hand cell is given by Eq. 6-62. Substituting for the concentration of each complex species from Eq. 6-58

$$C_{Cd} = [Cd^{2+}]_L + \beta_1[Cd^{2+}]_L[SCN^-] + \beta_2[Cd^{2+}]_L[SCN^-]^2 + \cdots \quad \textbf{6-64}$$

or

$$C_{Cd} = [Cd^{2+}]_L\{1 + \beta_1[SCN^-] + \beta_2[SCN^-]^2 + \cdots \qquad \textbf{6-65}$$

Since the total cadmium concentration $C_{Cd} = 1 \times 10^{-4}\ M$, we can solve for $[Cd^{2+}]_L$

$$[Cd^{2+}]_L = \frac{1 \times 10^{-4}}{\{1 + \beta_1[SCN^-] + \beta_2[SCN^-]^2 + \cdots\}} \qquad \textbf{6-66}$$

Substituting in Eq. 6-61

$$\Delta\mathscr{E} = \frac{RT}{2\mathscr{F}} \ln\{1 + \beta_1[SCN^-] + \beta_2[SCN^-]^2 + \cdots\} \qquad \textbf{6-67}$$

Defining the function enclosed in { } as $F_0(X)$, then

$$\Delta\mathscr{E} = 2.303\,\frac{RT}{2\mathscr{F}} \log F_0(X) \qquad \textbf{6-68}$$

From the observed values of $\Delta\mathscr{E}$, $\log F_0(X)$ may be calculated from Eq. 6-68. The equation for $F_0(X)$ may be written as

$$F_0(X) = 1 + \beta_1[SCN^-] + \beta_2[SCN^-]^2 + \cdots$$

This is the equation for a curve when $F_0(X)$ is plotted *vs.* $[SCN^-]$. Such a curve is shown for the data of Table 6-1 in Figure 6-2. The intercept of the plot can be seen to be unity, and the limiting slope should be β_1.

If the function $F_1(X)$ is defined

$$F_1(X) = \frac{(F_0(X) - 1)}{[SCN^-]} \qquad \textbf{6-69}$$

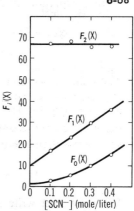

Figure 6-2 $F_i(X)$ values for the formation of cadmium thiocyanate complexes.

then
$$F_1(X) = \beta_1 + \beta_2[SCN^-] + \cdots$$

The intercept of a plot of $F_1(X)$ vs. $[SCN^-]$ gives a value of β_1 and the limiting slope should be β_2.

A similar definition of $F_2(X)$

$$F_2(X) = \frac{(F_1(X) - \beta_1)}{[SCN^-]} = \beta_2 + \beta_3[SCN^-] + \cdots \qquad \textbf{6-70}$$

A plot of $F_2(X)$ vs. $[SCN^-]$ should give β_2 as an intercept and a limiting slope of β_3.

For the cadmium thiocyanate system, the values of the stability constants obtained by this method were $\beta_1 = 10$ and $\beta_2 = 67$. Since the slope of $F_2(X)$ vs. $[SCN^-]$ is zero, this indicates no higher complexes exist over the range of concentrations for which data are presented. At higher thiocyanate ion concentrations, complexes containing three and four thiocyanate ions per cadmium ion have been detected.

This widely used graphical method was developed by Leden for potentiometric studies and was later applied to polarographic studies by DeFord and Hume.

Problems

6-1   Given the standard oxidation potentials for the half-reactions:

$$Fe^{2+}(aq) \rightleftharpoons Fe^{3+}(aq) + e^- \qquad \mathscr{E}^0 = -0.771$$
$$Ag(s) + Cl^-(aq) \rightleftharpoons AgCl(s) + e^- \qquad \mathscr{E}^0 = -0.222$$

(a) Calculate the equilibrium constant of the reaction

$$Ag(s) + Cl^-(aq) + Fe^{3+}(aq) \rightleftharpoons AgCl(s) + Fe^{2+}(aq)$$

(b) Calculate the standard free energy change at 25°C.

6-2   Given the standard oxidation potential of silver metal to silver ion at 25°C:

$$Ag(s) \rightleftharpoons Ag^+(aq) + e^- \qquad \mathscr{E}^0 = -0.799$$

and the solubility product constant for AgBr at 25°C

$$K_s{}^0(AgBr) = 4.9 \times 10^{-13}$$

What is the oxidation potential corresponding to the half-reaction?

$$Ag(s) + Br^-(aq) \rightleftharpoons AgBr(s) + e^-$$

6-3   Given the standard free energies of formation of the following ions at 25°C:

$MnO_4^-(aq)$	-107.4 kcal
$Mn^{2+}(aq)$	-54.4 kcal
$H_2O(l)$	-56.7 kcal
$H^+(aq)$	0.0 kcal
$H_2(g, 1\ atm)$	0.0 kcal

(a) What is the free energy change corresponding to the half-reaction

$$Mn^{2+}(aq) + 4 H_2O \rightleftarrows MnO_4^-(aq) + 8 H^+(aq) + 5e^-$$

(b) What is the oxidation potential?

6-4 Consider the cell composed of the hypothetical metal-metal perchlorate, $Me(ClO_4)_2$, half-cells as shown:

$$Me|Me(ClO_4)_2(2.00 \times 10^{-4} \, M), \, NaClO_4(0.5 \, M - X \, M), \, NaSCN(X \, M) \, ||$$

$$NaClO_4(0.5 \, M), \, Me(ClO_4)_2 \, (2.00 \times 10^{-4} \, M)|Me$$

The following e.m.f.'s were obtained at 25°C when $NaClO_4$ in the left-hand cell was replaced by NaSCN. Calculate the β values for the species necessary to explain these data.

[NaSCN]	$\Delta\mathscr{E}$
0.0500 M	0.0099 V
0.1000	0.0165
0.2000	0.0270
0.3000	0.0348
0.4000	0.0413
0.5000	0.0469

6-5 From the data presented in Tables 3-1 and 5-2, calculate the $\mathscr{E}^0$ values at 25°C for half-cells corresponding to the following reactions:
(a) $Ag \rightleftarrows Ag^+(aq) + e^-$
(b) $Ag + 2 NH_3(aq) \rightleftarrows Ag(NH_3)_2^+(aq) + e^-$
(c) $Cu + 4 NH_3(aq) \rightleftarrows Cu(NH_3)_4^{2+} + 2e^-$
(d) $Ag + I^-(aq) \rightleftarrows AgI(s) + e^-$
(e) $2 CH_3COO^-(aq) + H_2 \rightleftarrows 2 CH_3COOH(aq) + 2e^-$
(f) $OH^-(aq) + H_2 \rightleftarrows 2 H_2O + 2e^-$

6-6 From the data presented in Tables 3-1 and 5-2 calculate the equilibrium constant and the standard free energy change for the reaction at 25°C

$$Ni + 2 Ag(NH_3)_2^+(aq) \rightleftarrows Ni(NH_3)_4^{2+}(aq) + 2 Ag$$

6-7 From the data presented in Tables 3-1 and 5-2, what are the e.m.f. values of the following cells at 25°C?
(a) $Ni|Ni^{2+}(0.1 \, M)| \, |Cu^{2+}(0.05 \, M)|Cu$
(b) $Ag|AgCl(s), \, Cl^-(0.1 \, M)| \, |H^+(10^{-7} \, M)|H_2(1 \text{ atm}), Pt.$

6-8 What are the equilibrium constants and standard free energy changes for the following reactions at 25°C?
(a) $Ni^{2+}(aq) + Cu(s) \rightleftarrows Cu^{2+}(aq) + Ni(s)$
(b) $2 Ag + 2 HCl(aq) \rightleftarrows 2 AgCl(s) + H_2(g)$

APPENDIX

I. Equilibrium Constants of Acids and Bases at 25°C.*

ACIDS	Formula	K_1	K_2
	H_2CO_3	4.3×10^{-7}	5.6×10^{-11}
	HCN	4.9×10^{-10}	

ACIDS	Formula	K_1	K_2
	HF	6.8×10^{-4}	
	H_2S	9.1×10^{-8}	1.1×10^{-12}
	H_2SO_3	5×10^{-2}	1×10^{-7}
	$HC_2H_3O_2$	1.75×10^{-5}	
	$H_2C_2O_4$	5.9×10^{-2}	6.4×10^{-5}
	$HO_2CCH_2CO_2H$	1.51×10^{-3}	2.2×10^{-6}
	$Al(H_2O)_6^{3+}$	1.0×10^{-5}	
	$Cd(H_2O)_4^{2+}$	3×10^{-11}	
BASES	NH_3	1.79×10^{-5}	
	N_2H_4	8.7×10^{-7}	1.86×10^{-14}
	CH_3NH_2	5.2×10^{-4}	
	$NH_2CH_2CH_2NH_2$	1.38×10^{-4}	2.67×10^{-7}
	$C_2H_5NH_2$	4.7×10^{-4}	

II. Solubility Products of Slightly Soluble Compounds at 25°C.*

Formula	K_s^0	Formula	K_s^0
AgCl	1.78×10^{-10}	$Zn(OH)_2$	4.5×10^{-17}
AgBr	4.9×10^{-13}	$Pb(OH)_2$	4.2×10^{-15}
AgI	8.3×10^{-17}	$Sn(OH)_2$	3×10^{-27}
CaF_2	3.4×10^{-11}	HgO	3×10^{-26}
TlCl	1.78×10^{-4}	$BaSO_4$	1.0×10^{-10}
$AgBrO_3$	5.4×10^{-5}	$SrSO_4$	2.6×10^{-7}

III. Consecutive Equilibrium Constants for the Stepwise Formation of Complex Ions in the Temperature Range 20–25°C.*

Formula	$\log K_1$	$\log K_2$	$\log K_3$	$\log K_4$
$Ag(NH_3)_j^+$	3.20	3.83	—	—
$Cu(NH_3)_j^{2+}$	3.99	3.34	2.73	1.97
$Zn(NH_3)_j^{2+}$	2.18	2.25	2.31	1.96
$Hg(NH_3)_j^{2+}$	8.8	8.7	1.0	0.8
$Ag(CN)_j^{(1-j)}$	7.7	13.3	—	—
$Cd(CN)_j^{(2-j)}$	5.54	5.06	4.66	3.58
$Zn(OH)_j^{(2-j)}$	4.4	7.2	2.5	1.3
$Pb(OH)_j^{(2-j)}$	6.2	4.7	3.0	2.4
$Sn(OH)_j^{(2-j)}$	11.93	9.01	4.45	—
$Hg(OH)_j^{(2-j)}$	7.9	14.0	−0.8	—

* Taken from reference 2, Appendix VI, with permission of publisher.

IV. Oxidation Potentials at 25°C.*

Half-Reaction	$\mathscr{E}^0$, volts
$K \rightleftharpoons K^+ + e^-$	2.92
$Zn \rightleftharpoons Zn^{2+} + 2\,e^-$	0.76
$Cd \rightleftharpoons Cd^{2+} + 2\,e^-$	0.40
$Sn \rightleftharpoons Sn^{2+} + 2\,e^-$	0.14
$H_2 \rightleftharpoons 2\,H^+ + 2\,e^-$	0.00
$H_2S \rightleftharpoons S + 2\,H^+ + 2\,e^-$	-0.14
$H_2SO_3 + H_2O \rightleftharpoons SO_4{}^{2-} + 4\,H^+ + 2\,e^-$	-0.20
$S + 3\,H_2O \rightleftharpoons H_2SO_3 + 4\,H^+ + 4\,e^-$	-0.45
$2\,I^- \rightleftharpoons I_2 + 2\,e^-$	-0.53
$Ag \rightleftharpoons Ag^+ + e^-$	-0.799
$NO_2 + 2\,H_2O \rightleftharpoons NO_3{}^- + 2\,H^+ + e^-$	-0.81
$NO + 2\,H_2O \rightleftharpoons NO_3{}^- + 4\,H^+ + 3\,e^-$	-0.96
$2\,Br^- \rightleftharpoons Br_2 + 2\,e^-$	-1.06
$Mn^{2+} + 2\,H_2O \rightleftharpoons MnO_2 + 4\,H^+ + 2\,e^-$	-1.28
$2\,Cr^{3+} + 7\,H_2O \rightleftharpoons Cr_2O_7{}^{2-} + 14\,H^+ + 6\,e^-$	-1.32
$2\,Cl^- \rightleftharpoons Cl_2 + 2\,e^-$	-1.36
$Mn^{2+} + 4\,H_2O \rightleftharpoons MnO_4{}^- + 8\,H^+ + 5\,e^-$	-1.52
$Ce^{3+} \rightleftharpoons Ce^{4+} + e^-$	-1.61

* Taken from reference 1, Appendix VI, with permission of publisher.

V. Some Suggested Reading

(1) G. E. MacWood and F. H. Verhoek, "How Can You Tell Whether a Reaction Will Occur?" *Journal of Chemical Education*, **38**, 334 (1961).

(2) J. Arthur Campbell, *Why Do Chemical Reactions Occur?* Prentice-Hall, Inc., Englewood Cliffs, N.J., 1965.

(3) Gordon M. Harris, *Chemical Kinetics*, D. C. Heath Co., Boston, Mass., 1966.

(4) Edward L. King, *How Chemical Reactions Occur*, W. A. Benjamin, Inc., New York, N.Y., 1963

(5) James N. Butler, *Ionic Equilibrium*, Addison-Wesley Publishing Co., Inc., Reading, Mass., 1964.

(6) B. H. Mahan, *Elementary Chemical Thermodynamics*, W. A. Benjamin, Inc., New York, N.Y., 1963.

(7) W. L. Jolley, "The Use of Oxidation Potentials in Inorganic Chemistry," *Journal of Chemical Education*, **43**, 198 (1966).

(8) I. M. Kolthoff and P. J. Elving, *Treatise on Analytical Chemistry*, Volume I, Part I., Interscience Publishers, New York, N.Y., 1959.

The following chapters of this treatise are recommended:

(a) Chapter 7, "Chemical Equilibrium and the Thermodynamics of Reactions," by T. S. Lee.

(b) Chapter 11, "Concepts of Acids and Bases," by I. M. Kolthoff.

(c) Chapter 12, "Acid-Base Strength and Protolysis Curves in Water," by S. Bruckenstein and I. M. Kolthoff.

(d) Chapter 8, "Graphic Presentation of Equilibrium Data," by Lars G. Sillén.

(e) Chapter 17, "Solubility," by D. L. Leussing.

(9) F. J. C. Rossotti and H. Rossotti, *The Determination of Stability Constants*, McGraw-Hill, New York, N.Y., 1961.

(10) A. E. Martell and M. Calvin, *Chemistry of the Metal Chelate Compounds*, Prentice-Hall, Inc., New York, N.Y., 1952.

VI. Tabulations of Equilibrium Constants

(1) W. M. Latimer, *Oxidation Potentials*, 2nd ed., Prentice-Hall, Inc., New York, N.Y., 1952.

(2) L. G. Sillén and A. E. Martell, *Stability Constants*, Special Publication No. 17, The Chemical Society, London, 1964.

VII. Answers to Problems

2–1 $E^{\ddagger} = 27.4$ kcal/mole.

2–2 $E^{\ddagger} = 30.0$ kcal/mole.

2–3 $K_{eq} = 1.74$.

2–4 $\alpha = 0.635$.

2–5 $K_p = 21.7$ atm, $K_c = 0.187$ mole/liter.

2–6 $\beta\ 0.5\ P_t = 63.2$ atm, $\beta\ 0.1\ P_t = 4.94$ atm.

2–7 $K_c = 0.167$, 4.37 moles NO_2.

3–1 (a) $\Delta G° = -229.03$ kcal, $\Delta H° = -216.228$ kcal, $\Delta S° = 42.976$ e.u.

(b) $\Delta G° = -241.36$ kcal, $\Delta H° = -279.34$ kcal, $\Delta S° = -127.364$ e.u.

3–2 $\Delta H° = 3.08$ kcal, $\Delta G° = 5.75$ kcal, $\Delta S° = -3.56$ e.u.

3–3 $\Delta H° = 116.0$ kcal, $\Delta G° = 73.8$ kcal, $\Delta S° = 29.1$ e.u.

3–4 NH_3 decomposes.

3–5 $P_{NO} = 13.2$ atm, $P_{O_2} = 917$ atm, $P_{N_2} = 583$ atm.

3–6 Fraction CO_2 consumed 0.305;

   $p_{H_2O} = p_{CO} = 10.15$ atm, $p_{H_2} = 6.49$ atm, $p_{CO_2} = 23.1$ atm

3–7 $K = 50.8$.

4–1 (a) $pH = 3.05$, (b) $pH = 2.64$, (c) $pH = 8.08$,
   (h) $pH = 2.49$

4–2 (a) 0.0131, (b) 0.0185, (c) 0.0893, (d) 0.187.

4–3 (a) 0.152, 0.848; (b) 0.642, 0.358; (c) 0.985, 0.015.

4–4 (a) 0.092, (b) 4.43, (c) 4.46.

4–5 Fractions 0.091, 0.91, 7.6×10^{-6}; concentrations
   0.00182, 0.0182, 1.52×10^{-7}.

4–6 $1.17 \times 10^{-7}, 1.1 \times 10^{-6}, 1.1 \times 10^{-5}, 1.4 \times 10^{-4}$,
   8.4×10^{-4}.

4–7 0.001, 0.018, 4.4×10^{-7}.

5–1 $S = 3.8 \times 10^{-5}$, (b) 1.14×10^{-4}.

5–2 K_s from 41×10^{-8} to 130×10^{-8}, $K_s^\circ = 24.0 \times 10^{-8}$.

5–4 (b) $2.4 \times 10^{-4}, 3.2 \times 10^{-2}, 1.6 \times 10^{-1}$, (c) 1.737.

5–5 $K_s^\circ = 6.5 \times 10^{-11}, \beta_1^\circ = 20, \beta_2^\circ = 2.5 \times 10^5$.

6–1 $K = 1.91 \times 10^9, \Delta G^\circ = 12.65$ kcal.

6–2 $\mathcal{E}^\circ = -0.071$ volts.

6–3 (a) $\Delta G^\circ = 173.8$ kcal, (b) $\mathcal{E}^\circ = -1.51$ volt.

6–4 $\beta_1 = 21, \beta_2 = 53, \beta_3 = 112$.

6–5 (b) -0.37, (c) 0.33, (d) 0.152.

6–6 $K_{eq} = 2 \times 10^{28}$.

6–7 (a) 0.578, (b) -0.576.

6–8 $K_{eq} = 1.45 \times 10^{-20}, 3.0 \times 10^{-8}$.

Index

1 2 3 4 5 6 7 8 9 0